the 21-Day Wonder Diet

THE AUSTRALIAN Women's Weekly

Contents

The dieters

INTRODUCING PAMELA CLARK AND SARAH SCHWIKKARD, the Test Kitchen guinea pigs. Pamela, Test Kitchen Director, and Sarah, Test Kitchen Food Editor, embarked on a mission to try out the 21-day diet in order to get their bodies ship-shape in time for summer.

Working weeks jam-packed with functions, meetings and taste-testing rules Pamela's food routine. Like most Baby Boomers out there, her weekends revolve around tending to grandparent duties, socialising with family and friends, gardening, and the never-ending list of things to do around the house; this hectic schedule means that there is little time left to fuss over healthy eating. Pamela felt that it was time to get some balance back in her life, and what better opportunity to do it than when a diet cookbook is being developed at work.

Representing Generation Y, Sarah decided that it was time to lose the lumps and bumps she'd acquired from tasting food non-stop in the Test Kitchen. Partial to sugary foods, champagne and "grazing", Sarah's eating habits were in need of a serious shake-up. For this serial dieter, the thought of eating three healthy meals each day was rather confronting; she had to accept that weekends filled with indulgent dinners and drinks were about to become a thing of the past. Sarah admitted that part of her problem was her inability to be disciplined with routine; it was time for her to learn to restrain, and retrain, her body in order to kill the sugar cravings – once and for all.

Pamela lost 5.5kg in the 21 days and Sarah was not far behind with 5kg off her frame. They both found the diet so easy to stick to that they repeated it – again with fabulous results. The (former) guinea pigs are now ready to face summer feeling revitalised, fresh and fantastic.

A healthy-eating plan that is balanced, low-in-fat but high-in-taste: sound impossible? Well, it's not. We've developed a diet that doesn't mirror any of the "fad" diets on the market today; our key to success is a menu plan with less than 20g fat per day. British people eat an average of 60g to 80g of fat per day; by reducing this intake by around two-thirds, it is obvious why our diet is foolproof. Whether you want to lose weight for medical reasons, for a special upcoming event or just for your own wellbeing, this diet is for you.

ATTACK THE FAT

Fat is not our enemy. However, with obesity rates in the UK at an all-time high, it is important that we educate ourselves about fat, and recognise the difference between "good" and "bad" fats. You may have heard of saturated fats and trans fats: these are "bad" fats. Found in fatty meats, commercial cakes and deep-fried takeaway food, "bad" fats increase the risk of heart disease and contribute to high blood cholesterol. "Good" fats, like polyunsaturated fats and monounsaturated fats, are abundant in oils such as sunflower and olive, as well as salmon, tuna, nuts, lean meats and seeds; these fats can help lower blood cholesterol and reduce the risk of heart disease.

21 DAYS OF DISCIPLINE

If Pamela and Sarah can do this diet, anyone can. True to Women's Weekly style, the recipes we've developed (and tested to perfection) are easy-to-follow, there are no hard-to-find ingredients and, best of all, the diet is incredibly inexpensive; losing weight doesn't have to make your pockets lighter, just your body! We believe that it's imperative to eat in order to trim down; by eating three meals and two snacks per day, for 21 days, you'll find that you lose weight in a fashion that is good for your body – and the weight will stay off.

10
steps to diet success

Motivation

ARE YOU READY TO LOSE WEIGHT?

There's no point embarking on a lifestyle change unless you're mentally prepared. It's vital that you've thought carefully about why you want to lose weight and, most importantly, who you're losing weight for (the answer should be you). Without the commitment, the drive and the passion to achieve results for yourself with this diet, it will be a challenge to be successful.

WRITE A LIST

If you've recognised that you need a change, whether it's because your jeans don't zip up anymore, you're short of breath when you chase the kids around the park, or the photos from last Christmas make you cringe, then it's time to be pro-active and make a change. A good way to start is to write a list of things you like about yourself, and a list of things you're not too happy with; this will help clear your mind, and give you focus to start the diet.

SET A GOAL FOR YOURSELF

Perhaps it's a dress that you haven't been able to zip up for years, or you want to tone up your legs for some new summer shorts, by setting a goal, it gives you something to work towards; write it down on a piece of paper and stick it somewhere visible – like on your computer at work or on your mirror in the bathroom. Every time you look at it, it'll give you motivation, and remind you why you're doing the diet – for yourself.

2

FACTS ABOUT THE WONDER DIET

The diet is low in fat, it is below 20g fat per day; the average person in the UK eats 60g to 80g fat per day.

The diet is low in sugar, except for the natural sugars found in fruit.

The diet is moderate in iron; citrus juice (vitamin C) is used in the recipes for flavour and to help iron absorption.

This is a low-sodium (salt) diet so we've used fresh herbs for flavouring. Herbs also contain vitamins, minerals and anti-oxidants.

STOCKING UP

Out of sight, out of mind: this saying goes hand-in-hand with diet mentality. If you don't have any junk food in your cupboard, you won't be tempted to eat it. Fill your fridge, freezer and pantry with healthy foods, so even if you feel like a midnight snack, you'll be munching on a carrot stick, rather than a bag of chips.

ORGANISING YOUR LIFE

Not only do you need to be motivated and committed, it's paramount that you're organised and prepared for this diet. By being 100% prepared, it means that you don't give yourself a chance to slip back into bad habits. For example, if you know that Mondays are notoriously busy for you, then make dinner for Monday on Sunday night and pop it in the fridge or freezer. This means that you avoid coming home from work on Monday, tired and hungry, and reaching for the phone to order a pizza. You can always get your family involved, too; the recipes in this diet are all kid-friendly – if you're having a tuna salad for lunch, then so can they. Make a double quantity of the recipe and you'll find that you halve the time you spend in the kitchen.

SWAPPING DAYS

Feel free to swap days around on the diet to suit your lifestyle. For example, if you look at the menu for Day 6 and think that you would rather have the food from Day 11 instead, then just swap them around. Same goes for the snacks – feel free to chop and change. By making changes like this, you're making life easier for yourself, and you'll find it easier to stick to the diet.

Planning

Exercise

3

SWEAT IT OUT

Whether you like it or not, exercise is integral to weight loss. We're not talking about running marathons here, just regular, moderate exercise. Not only will exercising help you lose weight and tone your body, but it makes you feel good, too. Why? Well, when you exercise, your brain releases endorphins – nature's "happy pill". It's certainly a cheap and easy way to get a smile on your dial. So, if you're feeling a bit flat or you've had a bad day, the best thing you can do is go and do some exercise – it'll make you feel better in no time.

MAKE TIME FOR EXERCISE

Morning, noon or night, any time is a good time for fitness. If you're not a morning person, then how about taking the dog for a walk at sunset. Or, if you always work late at night, then get up half an hour earlier and put your exercise gear on. Lunchtime exercise is also a great way to fit it into your day; rather than eating lunch at your desk, walk down to a park bench and eat it there. Not only do you get a bit of exercise before you eat, but you also get a good dose of fresh air before you return to the office. Weekends are always a good time to get fit; instead of going out for coffee and cake, get a group of friends together and go for a long walk.

INCIDENTAL EXERCISE

There are lots of ways to fit "incidental exercise" into your day – this is exercise that isn't formal exercise, but it's all these extra bits of activity that you do that can make a difference. For example, take the stairs instead of the lift, park your car far away from the supermarket, or even better, leave your car at home and walk to the shops instead.

DID YOU KNOW that if you eat a 50g piece of milk chocolate, you need to walk briskly for over 60 minutes to burn off the calories?

FACTS ABOUT THE WONDER DIET
Drink at least 2 litres of water every day; include tea, coffee etc., in this count. We suggest you avoid alcohol-based drinks while you're on this diet.

Water

4

HYDRATION

It is paramount that you keep your body hydrated when you do the diet. Not enough water can do a number of things to you – apart from the obvious, and most severe, dehydration, a lack of water can make you tired and also give you headaches. By drinking at least 2 litres of water a day, you'll be keeping your body and mind in line. Water also aids with satiety (feeling full), and a glass of water is certainly better for you than a chocolate biscuit.

A SPARKLE IN YOUR EYES

It may sound too good to be true, but by drinking lots of water, you're helping your skin, hair and eyes to look great. People who drink a lot of water generally have a clear complexion, shiny hair and a sparkle in their eyes.

Scales

5

WEIGHTS AND MEASURES

The recipes in this diet have been carefully measured and triple-tested, so it is important to use the weights that we've given in the recipes, to ensure that you are getting the nutrition we intended. Take the guesswork out and invest in kitchen scales if you don't own them already; scales come in handy for weighing meat, poultry and seafood.
Flavour-enhancers like chilli, mustard, herbs and spices can be used with abandon as they contain a negligible amount of fat and kilojoules. Take care when using cooking-oil spray; a 1-second spray of oil is measured as 1g of fat, so apply sparingly.

WEIGH-IN

Weighing yourself every day will not give you a true reflection of your weight-loss; weight can fluctuate from day-to-day. It helps to be consistent with what you wear when you weigh-in, too – preferably weigh yourself naked to give a true indication of what you weigh, otherwise wear something lightweight. It's also good to weigh yourself at the same time, for example, 7am every Monday morning; and make sure you use the same set of scales every time.

SLEEP WELL, LOOK SWELL

It's important that you look after your body when you are on a diet. By depriving yourself of sleep, your energy stores become depleted and staying awake during the day becomes a real struggle. Keep your energy levels high and mood positive by getting at least eight hours sleep a night. You'll look better for it, too, with no tell-tale signs of tiredness, like dark circles under your eyes. A good night's sleep is also necessary to give your body time to repair; the human body is constantly working, using the nutrients it collects from your food to strengthen and recharge your muscles.

NIGHT-TIME WEIGHT-LOSS

Not only does a good rest give you energy, but it also helps you lose weight. While you sleep, your body burns calories (yes, it's true!); on average, you burn about 3.8kJ/0.9 calories per minute of sleep – there's no better excuse to get some shut-eye.

STOP SNORING

A very common problem among men and women alike, snoring, and sleep apnoea, is prevalent predominantly in overweight middle-aged males. Alcohol, caffeine, sleep deprivation and late-night eating are top things to avoid if you'd like a night without the disruption caused by snoring.

RELAX AND UNWIND

For many of us, falling asleep after a stressful, busy day is often with great effort; however, if you go to bed relaxed, chances are that you will sleep well. Drinking non-caffeinated herbal teas before you sleep, and burning aromatherapy oils in your bedroom, both assist in helping you relax before you go to bed. By creating a warm, soothing environment where you sleep, you will wake up feeling refreshed and ready for another day.

Sleep

STRATEGIC EATING

Holidays, birthday parties, work functions, dinner parties ... the list can go on and on – these are all events where over-eating is notorious. Being on a diet doesn't mean that you have to avoid attending special occasions, you simply need to make smart eating choices, ensuring that you don't become the pig of the party. If you're dining out, don't be shy to ask the waiter if you can alter the meal slightly to suit your dietary needs; for example, ask for sauces and dressings to be served on the side, grill fish instead of frying – it's all about strategic eating.

RESIST AND WIN

Nibbles and treats need to be resisted in order to achieve diet success; things like garlic bread at restaurants, chips and dips at parties and ice-cream at the movies are all laden with fat and sugar, and only provide temporary satisfaction. You're far better off to ignore these foods and enjoy your main meal, rather than filling up on the unnecessary side-dishes.

SLOWLY DOES IT

If you choose to have a glass of wine at a function, drink it slowly, rather than guzzling glass after glass. Alcohol, in particular beer, contains a lot of calories so opt for a dry white wine or champagne, if you can. The best option however, is to drink water; sparkling mineral water is surprisingly rewarding, not to mention a far cheaper option than alcohol.

CUT THE CAKE

This diet isn't based on torture and guilt; there may be times when you are dying for a taste of chocolate or something a little naughty, so, if the birthday cake looks too good to resist, go mad, have a tiny piece. Just bear in mind, that for any extra calories you consume, you need to do extra exercise to compensate.

7

FACTS ABOUT THE WONDER DIET
You can eat the bran and cranberry muesli (p32) every day of this diet instead of following our breakfast suggestions. Swap whole days around to suit your tastes in food, but don't mix and match lunches and dinners. Swap lunches for dinners (on the same day) if it suits your lifestyle better.

Special occasions

Support

STRESS RELIEVERS

It makes a great deal of difference if you have a "support team" by your side during the diet. Whether it's your partner, your next-door neighbour or a group of girls from work, a little bit of support goes a long way. There will be easy days, as well as hard days on the journey; sharing your thoughts, problems and excitement with the "team" will help decrease any stress or doubt you may be feeling. If you know you have a problem with discipline, having a group of people you feel you can turn to can be a fantastic way to ensure you don't slip back into old eating habits.

POSITIVE ATTITUDE

The art of positive thinking plays a big role in reaching goals in life, and achieving success in the diet is no exception. You need to retain a positive frame of mind throughout the diet; doing the diet should be a positive experience, and you should feel proud of yourself for committing to it. Be confident about your decision to change your lifestyle, and you will find that others will share in your confidence, too. Ignore any negativity that is directed at you in relation to your weight-loss.

DEAR DIARY

Another easy way to keep yourself on track is to write a journal – doing so helps you remain accountable for your actions; like they say, if you cheat, you're only cheating yourself. Every day, jot down how you felt about the meals you ate, the exercise you did, record your weight loss and any thoughts you want to share with yourself. As the days go by, you can flick back and reflect on the progress you have made.

FACT ABOUT THE WONDER DIET
If your diet partner is not on this diet to lose weight, they can add more protein and carbs.

Shopping

FACTS ABOUT THE WONDER DIET
This is a high-fibre diet; it's rich in vegetables and fruit. There are 5 servings of vegetables and 2 of fruit per day. The diet is high in calcium, achieved by including low-fat dairy products every day. There are three servings of seafood (fresh and canned) per week.

SOUND STRUCTURE
The best way to tackle the supermarket is to write a shopping list – and stick to it. We've made shopping even easier for you, by ensuring that there are no ingredients used in the 21-day diet plan that can't be found in a regular supermarket. By going to the shops with a structured list, you have no need to venture down the junk-food aisle. Shopping with a list in hand is efficient, and most likely to be cost-effective, too.

SHOP FULL
Avoid shopping on an empty stomach; if you're hungry, you're more likely to be tempted to buy the foods that you shouldn't eat.

NUTRITION KNOW-HOW
Checking the nutrition information panel on food labels is a good way to educate yourself about what you're eating. It's an interesting way to learn about the composition of different foods; information about energy (calories), protein, total fat, saturated fat, carbohydrate, sugar and sodium are displayed on this panel. Be wary of food labelled with claims of being "low-fat", "low-calorie" or "low-salt" – this is sometimes just a marketing strategy employed to catch out ignorant consumers.

IT PAYS TO HAVE TIME
Although not always possible to achieve, it's beneficial to go grocery shopping when it's not too busy, i.e., avoid Saturday mornings and late-night trading if you can. You want to be calm and relaxed when shopping to avoid having to make hasty decisions about what you put in your trolley.

10

A+ FOR EFFORT

If you want to sustain your weight loss, you need to put in effort. After being disciplined for 21 days and achieving fantastic results, you don't want to un-do all the hard work you've done; identify your vices, whether it's pizzas, chocolate bars or thick shakes, and steer clear.

INCREASE YOUR INTAKE

Once you've finished the diet, if you'd like to maintain the weight you are at, you can increase your kilojoule intake, as long as you continue to exercise. There is however, no reason why you can't repeat the diet, like Pamela and Sarah successfully did.

EMOTIONAL EATING

Be happy to eat, don't eat to be happy – it is crucial that you don't binge-eat or make poor food choices to compensate for any emotional imbalance, otherwise you will find it difficult to maintain your ideal weight. The best thing you can do for yourself if you're feeling down is to put on your exercise gear, and get some fresh air.

BREAKFAST FUEL

Eating breakfast doesn't stop after the 21-day diet; maintaining your weight will be a lot easier if you continue to eat three full meals per day. If you don't have time to cook or bake your breakfast every morning, you can always make a large batch of our bran and cranberry muesli (see recipe, p32), as a stand-by breakfast saviour.

SMILE

Remember who you're doing this for: you. Be positive, be proud and be happy that you're pro-active and making a better life for yourself.

Maintenance

Day 1 Menu

melon trio with fresh lime and yogurt | dijon chicken and salad wrap | spiced lamb cutlets with coriander pumpkin

melon trio with fresh lime and yogurt

preparation time 10 minutes **serves** 2
nutritional count per serving 0.8g total fat
(0.1g saturated fat); 573kJ (137 cal);
25.4g carbohydrate; 5.3g protein; 2.6g fibre

200g rockmelon, halved lengthways
200g honeydew melon, halved lengthways
200g watermelon, quartered crossways
2 tablespoons lime juice
½ cup (140g) skim-milk fruit-flavoured yogurt

1 Serve melons drizzled with juice, then dolloped with yogurt.

Sarah's diary
I woke up this morning quite excited about starting the diet. Wasn't disappointed at all with breakfast – it was yum. I was flat-out all morning so lunch was a welcome reprieve...it took me back to school days with the simple chicken and salad combo. Managed to get through the day without dipping my hand into the cookie jar (a first). I hope this motivation and discipline continues.

Pamela's diary
The first day of any diet can be a bit tricky for me; it always takes me three days to get into a routine. On the first day, I go through various stages, first feeling enthusiastic, then second, thinking, maybe I should start the following day, or even the following week. Procrastination should be my middle name. Anyway, here we go.

Choose whatever yogurt flavour you like; passionfruit flavour goes well with these fruits. Did you know melons are one of the best of all fruits. They're gentle on your digestive system and full of hydrating water and minerals.

snack 1 small
red capsicum with
1 tablespoon low-fat
cottage cheese

If you're one of those people who can't eat raw capsicum, then swap this snack for another in this book.
The wraps can be made in the morning to take to work; you can use any leafy greens you like in place of the spinach.

dijon chicken and salad wrap

200g chicken breast fillet
cooking-oil spray
1 tablespoon skim-milk natural yogurt
1 teaspoon dijon mustard
2 wholemeal wraps (60g)
20g baby spinach
1 small tomato (90g), sliced thinly
1 small carrot (70g), grated coarsely

1 Spray chicken with cooking oil; cook chicken in heated small frying pan. Cool; shred coarsely.
2 Combine chicken in medium bowl with yogurt and mustard.
3 Divide chicken mixture between wraps; top with remaining ingredients. Roll to enclose filling.

preparation time 10 minutes
cooking time 15 minutes **serves** 2
nutritional count per serving 3.8g total fat
(0.7g saturated fat); 932kJ (223 cal);
17.9g carbohydrate; 27.4g protein; 3.2g fibre

spiced lamb cutlets with coriander pumpkin

200g butternut pumpkin, peeled, cut into 1cm pieces
125g can chickpeas, rinsed, drained
½ cup (60g) frozen baby peas
2 tablespoons fresh coriander leaves
4 french-trimmed lamb cutlets (200g)
2 teaspoons curry powder
cooking-oil spray
⅓ cup (80ml) light coconut milk
2 tablespoons chicken stock
1 clove garlic, crushed

1 Preheat oven to 200°C/180°C fan-forced.
2 Roast pumpkin in small, shallow baking dish, uncovered, 10 minutes. Add chickpeas and peas; cook, uncovered, about 5 minutes or until pumpkin is tender. Remove from oven; sprinkle with coriander.
3 Meanwhile, sprinkle lamb with curry powder. Spray lamb with cooking oil. Cook lamb in heated medium frying pan; remove from pan.
4 Add coconut milk, stock and garlic to same pan, bring to the boil, stirring; remove from heat.
5 Serve pumpkin mixture and lamb drizzled with coconut sauce.

We used a mild curry powder for flavour but use what you like. Freeze any leftover coconut milk and store it in user-friendly portions for future meals.

preparation time 15 minutes
cooking time 15 minutes serves 2
nutritional count per serving 9.3g total fat (5.7g saturated fat); 978kJ (234 cal); 16.6g carbohydrate; 18.2g protein; 5.4g fibre

snack 1 small apple

Day 2 Menu

cheesy corn on rye | potato, tuna and egg salad | chilli con carne

cheesy corn on rye

preparation time 5 minutes
cooking time 30 seconds **serves** 2
nutritional count per serving 4.6g total fat
(1.7g saturated fat); 1120kJ (268 cal);
42.2g carbohydrate; 10.6g protein; 7.2g fibre

310g can corn kernels, rinsed, drained
2 tablespoons ricotta cheese
40g baby spinach leaves
2 slices rye bread (90g), toasted

1 Heat corn in medium bowl in microwave oven on HIGH
(100%) for about 30 seconds; stir in cheese and spinach.
2 Serve toast topped with corn mixture.

Sarah's diary

Got up at the crack of dawn to go for a walk – I couldn't believe the number of people and dogs out and about at that time. Absolutely loved breakfast, was quick to prepare and corn is one of my faves. The exercise must've got my metabolism moving because I devoured lunch in a flash. Dinner consumed while watching the news – trying to eat a bit earlier than usual. My housemates were most impressed (and perhaps shocked) that I didn't take them up on their offer of chocolate cake for dessert.

Pamela's diary

I woke up hungry this morning, and not feeling energetic enough to go for a walk. I must 'fess up to having a small glass of white wine with the family last night, just to be sociable. All three meals today were filling and tasty, but we also had a lot of food to be tasted in the Test Kitchen – it's not easy being on a diet around here.

Toast is best "done" on one side only for this kind of topping.

Make sure you prick the potatoes all over with a fork if you're cooking them in the microwave oven.
Salad can be made the night before – keep it in the fridge.

LUNCH

potato, tuna and egg salad

preparation time 5 minutes
cooking time 10 minutes **serves** 2
nutritional count per serving 7.5g total fat
(2.4g saturated fat); 1150kJ (275 cal);
18.9g carbohydrate; 30.7g protein; 3.9g fibre

6 baby new potatoes (240g)
100g green beans, trimmed, halved crossways
2 tablespoons skim-milk natural yogurt
1 teaspoon finely grated lemon rind
2 teaspoons lemon juice
185g can tuna in springwater, drained, flaked
3 green onions, sliced finely
1 tablespoon coarsely chopped fresh flat-leaf parsley
2 hard-boiled eggs, halved

1 Boil, steam or microwave potatoes and beans, separately, until tender; drain, cool.
2 Meanwhile, make dressing by combining yogurt, rind and juice in medium bowl.
3 Quarter potatoes; add to dressing with tuna, onion and parsley, stir to combine. Serve salad topped with egg.

snack 1 small banana

snack 200g rockmelon

chilli con carne

preparation time 10 minutes
cooking time 30 minutes **serves** 2
nutritional count per serving 7.9g total fat
(2.9g saturated fat); 1586kJ (378 cal);
43.5g carbohydrate; 28.6g protein; 8.3g fibre

⅓ cup (65g) brown rice
cooking-oil spray
1 small brown onion (80g), chopped finely
1 clove garlic, crushed
180g lean beef mince
1 teaspoon ground cumin
1 teaspoon dried chilli flakes
400g can diced tomatoes
2 tablespoons tomato paste
½ cup (125ml) beef stock
125g can four bean mix, rinsed, drained
2 tablespoons skim-milk natural yogurt
¼ cup coarsely chopped fresh flat-leaf parsley

This is a great recipe (both the rice and the mince mixture) to cook in large batches, ready to freeze in user-friendly portions. Freeze any leftover tomato paste or stock.

1 Cook rice in medium saucepan of boiling water until tender; drain.
2 Meanwhile, spray medium frying pan with cooking oil; cook onion and garlic over heat, stirring, until onion softens. Add beef and spices; cook, stirring, until beef is browned.
3 Add undrained tomatoes, paste and stock; bring to a boil. Reduce heat; simmer, covered, 10 minutes. Uncover; simmer about 10 minutes or until mixture thickens slightly. Stir in beans.
4 Serve rice and chilli con carne topped with yogurt. Sprinkle with parsley.

Day 3 Menu

mango lassi | roast beef and coleslaw on rye | sumac fish with couscous salad

mango lassi

preparation time 10 minutes **serves** 2
nutritional count per serving 3.0g total fat
(1.7g saturated fat); 849kJ (203 cal);
32.6g carbohydrate; 9.6g protein; 2.3g fibre

1 medium mango (430g), peeled, chopped coarsely
1 cup (250ml) buttermilk
⅓ cup (95g) skim-milk fruit-flavoured yogurt
2 tablespoons lime juice

1   Blend ingredients until smooth.

Sarah's diary
Trying to cut out my morning coffee on the way to work is proving to be a challenge – I had no idea how reliant I was on the caffeine to wake me up. Thankfully, the mango lassi was lovely. The sandwich was nice; I cooked my own beef because I'm not a fan of the deli-bought beef slices. Dinner was very filling – the weather was still balmy when I got home, so I cooked my fish on the bbq. Could've killed for a gin & tonic to wash it all down with, though.

Pamela's diary
More tastings today, which involved chocolate: I did taste the tiniest amounts possible, though. More confessions – I broke the weigh-yourself-once-a-week rule this morning, based on the feeling that my skirt felt slightly less snug than usual, and, to my delight, I have lost 0.6kg in just two days, despite the glass of wine and the tastings. I know daily weight can see-saw between one and two kilos, but I just know I've lost weight.

Make sure the mango you use is properly ripe, and, if you like, use all buttermilk and forget about the yogurt.

Use whatever cabbage you like; try the chinese variety (wombok), it's easy to shred finely. You can buy the roast beef, already cooked, from any deli.
Make the coleslaw the night before, then make the sandwich at lunch time the next day.

roast beef and coleslaw on rye

preparation time 10 minutes **serves** 2
nutritional count per serving 9.8g total fat
(2.6g saturated fat); 1731kJ (415cal);
51.1g carbohydrate; 25.0g protein; 9.7g fibre

1 cup (80g) finely shredded cabbage
1 small carrot (70g), grated coarsely
2 green onions, chopped finely
¼ cup (75g) 97% fat-free mayonnaise
1 tablespoon lemon juice
4 slices rare roast beef (120g)
4 slices rye bread (180g)

1   Combine cabbage, carrot, onion, mayonnaise and juice in medium bowl.
2   Divide beef between two slices of bread; top with coleslaw, then remaining bread.

snack 2 corn thins with
½ small sliced tomato

Use any firm fish that's in season, it's cheaper that way. Sumac is a type of Middle-Eastern spice, now available from supermarkets. The flavour is slightly tart. If you can't find the spice, cook the fish without it.

snack 1 small pear

sumac fish with couscous salad

cooking-oil spray
1 small red onion (100g), chopped finely
1 clove garlic, crushed
2 small green zucchinis (180g),
    sliced diagonally
125g cherry or grape tomatoes
¼ cup coarsely chopped fresh mint
½ cup (125ml) vegetable stock
½ cup (100g) couscous
320g firm white fish fillets
2 teaspoons sumac
1 lemon

1 Spray medium frying pan with cooking oil; cook onion and garlic over heat, stirring, 1 minute. Add zucchini and tomatoes; cook, stirring occasionally, about 10 minutes or until vegetables soften. Remove from heat; stir in mint.
2 Bring stock to a boil in small saucepan; remove from heat, stir in couscous, stand 5 minutes. Stir into zucchini mixture.
3 Meanwhile, preheat grill. Sprinkle fish with sumac; grill until cooked, turning once.
4 Serve couscous topped with fish and lemon wedges.

preparation time 10 minutes
cooking time 20 minutes serves 2
nutritional count per serving 5.6g total fat (1.4g saturated fat); 1739kJ (416 cal); 45.4g carbohydrate; 42.4g protein; 5.2g fibre

Day 4 Menu

bran and cranberry muesli | roasted sweet potato and tuna salad | warm tandoori chicken salad

bran and cranberry muesli

preparation time 5 minutes **serves** 2
nutritional count per serving 1.7g total fat
(0.4g saturated fat); 606kJ (145cal);
24.0g carbohydrate; 6.0g protein; 4.5g fibre

1 cup (90g) rolled oats
¾ cup (55g) All-Bran
¼ cup (35g) dried cranberries
⅔ cup (160ml) skim milk
½ cup (75g) fresh blueberries

1 Combine oats, bran and cranberries in small bowl to
make muesli mixture.
2 Place ⅓ cup muesli in each bowl; top with
milk and berries.
Store remaining muesli in an airtight container for
Day 12 and Day 20.

Sarah's diary
*First taste of All Bran in my
life this morning – I have
always steered well clear of
it, but it's actually not that
bad. I couldn't get any fresh
blueberries, so used thawed
frozen berries instead. We
had so many tastings in
the Kitchen today; I held
a teaspoon in my hand to
taste, rather than the usual
dessertspoon! Prepared
lunch last night, was quick
and easy, and tasted great
today. Met friends after
work for drinks, and settled
for a mineral water rather
than a riesling – a healthier,
and a far cheaper, option.*

Pamela's diary
*Feeling good, not hungry;
even went for a brisk walk
this morning. Breakfast and
lunch were great, but we
weren't happy with the
tandoori chicken for dinner:
we've had a play with the
recipe, you'll love it now. Last
night, just to be sociable, I
ate an olive and a dolmades,
and was overcome by the
oiliness; last week I would
have scoffed at least six
olives, and who knows how
many dolmades. It really
doesn't take the body long
to start cleaning up its act.*

If you don't want to use
dried cranberries, use
sultanas or raisins instead.

This recipe makes enough for 6 servings. If you don't feel like making some of the breakfasts we suggest, you can always have this muesli instead; remember, it's a ⅓ cup serving. You can always make a larger batch and keep it in an airtight container in the fridge.

Substitute any type of pumpkin for the sweet potato, if you like. It's best to prepare the ingredients the night before, then make the salad in the morning for lunch.

roasted sweet potato and tuna salad

preparation time 10 minutes (plus cooling time)
cooking time 20 minutes **serves** 2
nutritional count per serving 2.6g total fat
(0.8g saturated fat); 1195kJ (286 cal);
37.0g carbohydrate; 25.1g protein; 6.2g fibre

1 medium sweet potato (400g), cut into 2cm pieces
2 teaspoons finely grated orange rind
185g can tuna in springwater, drained, flaked
80g baby rocket leaves
1 large orange (300g), peeled, segmented
2 tablespoons orange juice
1 tablespoon light soy sauce
½ small red onion (50g), sliced thinly

1 Preheat oven to 180°C/160°C fan-forced.
2 Place sweet potato on oven tray; sprinkle with rind. Roast, uncovered, about 20 minutes; cool.
3 Combine sweet potato with remaining ingredients in medium bowl.

snack 1 small carrot

Chicken tenderloins are available from most supermarkets. You can use the same weight of lean chicken breast fillet and cut the fillet into long thin strips for quick cooking.

warm tandoori chicken salad

⅓ cup (95g) skim-milk natural yogurt
⅓ cup coarsely chopped fresh coriander
2 tablespoons lemon juice
6 small pappadums (20g)
280g chicken tenderloins
2 tablespoons tandoori powder
cooking-oil spray
100g baby spinach leaves
½ cucumber (130g), halved lengthways,
   sliced thickly
125g yellow teardrop tomatoes

1 Combine yogurt, coriander and juice in small bowl.
2 Cook pappadums in microwave oven on MEDIUM (50%) for about 40 seconds; break into pieces.
3 Sprinkle chicken with tandoori powder; spray with cooking oil. Cook chicken on heated grill plate (or grill or barbecue). Slice thickly.
4 Combine spinach, cucumber and tomatoes in medium bowl; add chicken. Serve salad sprinkled with pappadums, then drizzled with coriander yogurt.

preparation time 15 minutes
cooking time 10 minutes **serves** 2
nutritional count per serving 4.8g total fat (1.0g saturated fat); 1053kJ (252 cal); 10.7g carbohydrate; 38.7g protein; 4.4g fibre

snack 125g strawberries

Day 5 Menu

tomato and egg muffin | ricotta, basil and ham wrap | sesame beef stir-fry

tomato and egg muffin

preparation time 5 minutes
cooking time 5 minutes **serves** 2
nutritional count per serving 7.3g total fat
(1.9g saturated fat); 953kJ (228 cal);
24.2g carbohydrate; 14.5g protein; 3.9g fibre

cooking-oil spray
2 eggs
2 multigrain english muffins, split
1 small tomato (90g), sliced thinly
2 teaspoons balsamic vinegar

1 Spray medium frying pan with cooking oil. Fry eggs until cooked as you like.
2 Meanwhile, toast muffins.
3 Divide tomato between two muffin halves; sprinkle with vinegar, top with eggs, then remaining muffin halves.

Sarah's diary
Arrived at work to find bags upon bags of sweets for the kids' party cake book we're working on. Usually, I would have nose-dived into the pile of sugar, but I just kept on walking. Breakfast was yum; kept me going all morning. Ate my lunch in the local park, then went for a stroll to get my legs moving…they say that every bit counts! Stir-fry for dinner took next to no time to make, which was great after a long day at work. I think my boyfriend is quite envious of all this delicious food I'm eating – perhaps he'll join me!

Pamela's diary
Happy with the egg and tomato muffin for breakfast and loved the wrap at lunch time. The stir-fry for dinner was spot-on – it is my favourite meal so far, with just the right balance of flavours and chilli heat, and, I'm sure if you cooked this for people not on a diet, they wouldn't know the difference. More chocolate testing today, and we've started work on another party cake book, the Test Kitchen is littered with sweets – that tests us.

You can cut out another gram of fat by poaching the eggs in gently simmering water.

ricotta, basil and ham wrap

preparation time 5 minutes
cooking time 3 minutes **serves** 2
nutritional count per serving 6g total fat
(2.8g saturated fat); 930kJ (222 cal);
24.9g carbohydrate; 15.4g protein; 3.4g fibre

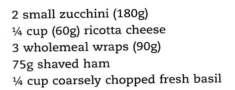

2 small zucchini (180g)
¼ cup (60g) ricotta cheese
3 wholemeal wraps (90g)
75g shaved ham
¼ cup coarsely chopped fresh basil

1 Preheat sandwich press.
2 Slice zucchini lengthways into ribbons using a
vegetable peeler.
3 Divide cheese among wraps; top with zucchini,
ham and basil. Roll to enclose.
4 Toast wraps in sandwich press for about 3 minutes;
cut in half to serve.

It's not vital to "toast" the wrap
in a sandwich press, but it
does give it a bit of a crisp
texture. Make the wrap in the
morning ready for lunch.

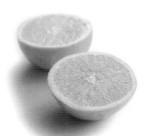

snack 1 medium orange

sesame beef stir-fry

½ cup (100g) couscous
½ cup (125ml) boiling water
2 teaspoons sesame seeds
180g rump steak, sliced thinly
1 small red onion (100g), cut into wedges
1 clove garlic, crushed
1 baby buk choy (150g), quartered
1 fresh long red chilli, sliced thinly
2 tablespoons beef stock
2 tablespoons oyster sauce
2 tablespoons light soy sauce
150g snow peas, sliced thinly

1   Combine couscous with the water in medium heatproof bowl, cover; stand 5 minutes.
2   Meanwhile, toast sesame seeds in heated wok about 30 seconds; transfer to small bowl.
3   Stir-fry beef in heated wok until browned; transfer to another small bowl.
4   Stir-fry onion in heated wok 1 minute. Add garlic, buk choy and chilli; stir-fry 1 minute. Add stock, sauces and beef; stir-fry until hot. Remove from heat; stir in peas.
5   Serve couscous topped with stir-fry and sprinkled with sesame seeds.

preparation time 10 minutes
(plus standing time)
cooking time 10 minutes serves 2
nutritional count per serving 5.6g total fat
(2.1g saturated fat); 1643kJ (393 cal);
51.3g carbohydrate; 31.3g protein; 4.1g fibre

snack 2 apricots, plums
or kiwifruit

Day 6 Menu

corn fritters | asparagus frittata with rocket | linguine marinara

corn fritters

preparation time 10 minutes
cooking time 10 minutes **serves** 2
nutritional count per serving 6.1g total fat
(1.4g saturated fat); 1476kJ (353 cal);
50.4g carbohydrate; 19.3g protein; 8.4g fibre

1 egg
310g can corn kernels, rinsed, drained
½ small red onion (50g), sliced thinly
½ cup (80g) wholemeal self-raising flour
⅓ cup (80ml) skim milk
cooking-oil spray
⅓ cup (65g) low-fat cottage cheese

1 Whisk egg in medium bowl; stir in corn, onion, flour and milk.
2 Spray large frying pan with cooking oil. Pour ⅓-cup of batter into heated pan; cook about 2 minutes or until bubbles appear. Turn fritters; cook until lightly browned on the other side.
3 Serve warm fritters dolloped with cheese; sprinkle with fresh dill or parsley, if you like.

Sarah's diary
My usual Saturday morning breakfast at the café downstairs was canned this morning, made the corn fritters instead and was not disappointed. Still managed to read the newspapers and have a peppermint tea at the café in the afternoon. Lunch was good; I loved the asparagus. Had invited friends over for dinner, so I just doubled the recipe for the marinara – everyone was thrilled that they too were eating a low-fat feast. I joined in for a glass of wine, but stopped after one.

Pamela's diary
I shared the corn fritters with my two granddaughters this morning – very well-received by all. Loved the frittata, but marinara is not my favourite thing in life. I love seafood, but prefer it unadorned. My local seafood shop usually does a really outstanding seafood mix, but this week it missed the mark for me; mind you, I ate the lot. If you like, you could use just prawns instead of the mix.

If you'd rather cook fresh corn, the easiest way is to coat the cob lightly with cooking oil spray, then cook it over the barbecue or on a griddle pan, turning the cob until it's lightly charred all over. Then, place the cob on a board and slice off the kernels.

If the handle of your frying pan is not heatproof, cover it with aluminium foil before placing it under the grill.

Frittata is delicious served warm, but if you like it cold, and want to take it to work, make it the evening before, keep it in the fridge, then wrap it in plastic the next morning.

LUNCH

asparagus frittata with rocket

preparation time 10 minutes
cooking time 15 minutes **serves** 2
nutritional count per serving 6.3g total fat
(1.8g saturated fat); 614kJ (147 cal);
5.4g carbohydrate; 16.3g protein; 1.9g fibre

cooking-oil spray
1 small red onion (100g), sliced thinly
170g asparagus, trimmed, cut into 2cm lengths
2 eggs
2 egg whites
2 tablespoons low-fat cottage cheese
40g baby rocket leaves
2 tablespoons lemon juice
2 teaspoons drained baby capers, rinsed

1 Preheat grill.
2 Spray small frying pan with cooking oil; cook onion over heat, stirring, 1 minute. Add asparagus; cook, stirring, 2 minutes.
3 Meanwhile, combine eggs, egg whites and cheese in a medium jug. Pour over asparagus mixture in pan. Cook, uncovered, about 5 minutes or until frittata is browned underneath.
4 Place pan under grill for about 5 minutes or until frittata is set.
5 Combine remaining ingredients in medium bowl; serve frittata with salad.

snack 2 passionfruit

This is a really simple recipe. There's only one thing to be careful of – don't overcook the seafood – if you do, it will be tough and leathery.

Use any pasta shape you like – and don't overcook it either. Cooked pasta with a little bit of bite left in it is better for your digestive system.

preparation time 5 minutes
cooking time 15 minutes **serves** 2
nutritional count per serving 7.2g total fat
(1.8g saturated fat); 2387kJ (571 cal);
61.9g carbohydrate; 60.1g protein; 6.4g fibre

linguine marinara

150g linguine pasta
400g uncooked seafood mix
1 small brown onion (80g), chopped finely
2 cloves garlic, crushed
1 fresh small red thai chilli, chopped finely
400g can diced tomatoes
⅓ cup coarsely chopped fresh flat-leaf parsley

1 Cook pasta in large saucepan of boiling water until tender; drain.
2 Meanwhile, cook seafood mix in heated large frying pan, stirring, for 2 minutes; drain.
3 Add onion, garlic and chilli to same heated pan; cook, stirring, about 5 minutes or until onion softens. Add undrained tomatoes; cook, 5 minutes. Return seafood to pan; cook, stirring occasionally, for about 2 minutes. Stir in parsley.
4 Serve pasta with marinara sauce.

snack 1 small apple

Day 7 Menu

date loaves | warm roasted vegie salad | pork cutlets with chickpea puree

date loaves

preparation time 10 minutes
cooking time 20 minutes **serves** 2
nutritional count per serving 6.8g total fat
(1.5g saturated fat); 1183kJ (283 cal);
46.4g carbohydrate; 8.2g protein; 2.2g fibre

cooking-oil spray
1 egg white
2 teaspoons vegetable oil
½ cup (75g) self-raising flour
⅓ cup (80ml) skim milk
1 tablespoon finely chopped dried dates
1 tablespoon brown sugar
1 tablespoon ricotta cheese

1 Preheat oven to 180°C/160°C fan-forced. Spray two holes of ½-cup (125ml) rectangular or round muffin pan with cooking oil.
2 Whisk egg white with a fork in medium bowl; stir in oil, flour, milk, dates and sugar, do not overmix. Divide mixture between pan holes.
3 Bake about 20 minutes. Serve warm loaves with cheese.

Sarah's diary
Dragged boyfriend out of bed bright and early to go for a walk to the beach. Even though there were complaints about "being up too early for a Sunday", I think he secretly enjoyed the fresh air. Got home and made the date loaves – such a great breakfast. Went with friends for a picnic at lunchtime, so I just packed up my vegie salad and took it with me. After one week of this diet, I'm feeling great; I probably look the same, but I feel a lot healthier.

Pamela's diary
Those date loaves are just divine, especially eaten warm. If I could be trusted not to eat them at random, I'd make quite a lot and freeze them, they would thaw really well in a microwave oven – I guess they'd take up to a minute to reheat. I've always been a fan of roasted vegie salads, but with lashings of olive oil; I love them hot, warm or cold.

Instead of roasting the vegies, you can char-grill them on a barbecue or a grill pan for a more smoky flavour.
The salad can be made a day ahead, then warmed through in a microwave oven. Add the cheese last.

LUNCH

warm roasted vegie salad

preparation time 10 minutes
cooking time 25 minutes **serves** 2
nutritional count per serving 3.2g total fat
(1.5g saturated fat); 698kJ (167 cal);
20.8g carbohydrate; 10.0g protein; 7.0g fibre

2 flat mushrooms (160g), halved
1 small sweet potato (250g), cut into 4cm pieces
1 small red capsicum (150g), cut into 4cm pieces
2 small tomatoes (180g), quartered
2 cloves garlic, chopped coarsely
¼ cup coarsely chopped fresh flat-leaf parsley
50g baby rocket leaves
1 tablespoon balsamic vinegar
2 tablespoons ricotta cheese

1 Preheat oven to 220°C/200°C fan-forced.
2 Combine vegetables and garlic in large baking dish. Roast, uncovered, about 25 minutes.
3 Combine roasted vegetables with parsley, rocket and vinegar in large bowl.
4 Serve salad sprinkled with cheese.

snack 100g skim-milk
fruit-flavoured yogurt

preparation time 10 minutes
cooking time 10 minutes **serves** 2
nutritional count per serving 7.2g total fat
(1.7g saturated fat); 1225kJ (293 cal);
16.0g carbohydrate; 37.3g protein; 7.1g fibre

DINNER

pork cutlets with chickpea puree

2 x 125g cans chickpeas, rinsed, drained
2 tablespoons lemon juice
2 cloves garlic, crushed
1 teaspoon ground fennel
⅓ cup (80ml) warm water
2 pork cutlets (470g), trimmed
cooking-oil spray
5 red radishes (300g), cut into matchsticks
½ cucumber (130g), chopped coarsely
⅓ cup coarsely chopped fresh flat-leaf parsley

1 Process chickpeas, juice, garlic and fennel until combined. Add the water; process until smooth.
2 Spray pork with cooking oil; cook pork on heated grill plate (or grill or barbecue).
3 Meanwhile, combine remaining ingredients in medium bowl.
4 Serve pork with salad and chickpea puree.

snack 125g grapes

Day 8 Menu

berry smoothie | lentil, tuna and tomato salad | crunchy chicken salad cups

berry smoothie

preparation time 5 minutes **serves** 2
nutritional count per serving 0.5g total fat
(0.2g saturated fat); 711kJ (170 cal);
26.9g carbohydrate; 12.2g protein; 3.4g fibre

250g strawberries
½ cup (75g) fresh or frozen blueberries
1 cup (250ml) skim milk
¾ cup (200g) skim-milk fruit-flavoured yogurt

1 Blend ingredients until smooth.

Sarah's diary
Smoothie tasted good, ate my snack at breakfast, too as I felt a bit peckish. Had more tastings for the chocolate book we're working on – Pamela and I were very restrained (I think everyone at work is starting to believe that we're taking this diet seriously!). None of the food has tasted diet-like yet: I'm surprised, because there's so little fat in the recipes. Ate dinner before going to a work function, which was a good move, otherwise I would've eaten all the beautiful canapés they were serving.

Pamela's diary
Clean, clean, clean is how I feel, and just a little bit smug and worthy; I'm certainly not hungry, and I'm certainly losing weight, what more can a girl ask for. Just over one third of the way there and I've lost two kilos, and am feeling very well. Back to work today, some kind person even commented on my weight loss.

You decide on the berry combination – they're all really good for you. Match the flavours with the yogurt.

50

snack 2 cups plain popcorn
Popcorn is a great snack –
even without the butter. Put
2 tablespoons of popping corn
into a large saucepan, cover with
a tightly fitting lid. Turn the heat
to high and wait for the popping
to start. Turn off the heat and wait
for the popping to stop before
removing the lid. This will give
you 2 cups of popcorn.

LUNCH

lentil, tuna and tomato salad

preparation time 10 minutes **serves** 2
nutritional count per serving 2.7g total fat
(0.8g saturated fat); 911kJ (218 cal);
18.3g carbohydrate; 26.7g protein; 6.3g fibre

400g can brown lentils, rinsed, drained
185g can tuna in springwater, drained, flaked
½ cucumber (130g), chopped coarsely
2 small tomatoes (180g), chopped coarsely
2 green onions, sliced thinly
⅓ cup coarsely chopped fresh flat-leaf parsley
1 clove garlic, crushed
2 tablespoons lemon juice
¼ cup (45g) drained cornichons, halved

1 Combine ingredients in medium bowl.

This is a perfectly portable
lunch. It can be made a
day ahead.

preparation time 10 minutes (plus cooling time)
cooking time 10 minutes **serves** 2
nutritional count per serving 4.5g total fat
(1.1g saturated fat); 895kJ (214 cal);
4.3g carbohydrate; 36.1g protein; 5.5g fibre

DINNER

crunchy chicken salad cups

220g chicken breast fillet
cooking-oil spray
½ cup (100g) low-fat cottage cheese
3 trimmed celery stalks (300g), chopped coarsely
4 green onions, sliced thinly
2 teaspoons coarsely chopped fresh dill
1 clove garlic, crushed
6 small iceberg lettuce leaves

1 Spray chicken with cooking oil; cook chicken in heated small frying pan. Remove from heat; cool.
2 Shred chicken coarsely; combine in medium bowl with cheese, celery, onion, dill and garlic.
3 Divide chicken mixture among lettuce leaves.

snack 1 small banana

Day 9 Menu

spinach omelette | turkey and cranberry wrap | prosciutto-wrapped lamb with roasted potatoes

spinach omelette

preparation time 5 minutes
cooking time 5 minutes **serves** 2
nutritional count per serving 5.9g total fat
(1.8g saturated fat); 882kJ (211 cal);
21.2g carbohydrate; 16.3g protein; 4.0g fibre

1 egg
4 egg whites
2 green onions, chopped finely
cooking-oil spray
30g baby spinach leaves
2 tablespoons coarsely chopped fresh mint
2 slices rye bread (90g), toasted
1 tablespoon ricotta cheese

1 Whisk egg, egg whites and onion in small jug.
2 Spray small frying pan with cooking oil; heat pan.
Pour egg mixture into pan; cook, tilting pan, until
mixture is almost set. Sprinkle spinach and mint
over half the omelette; fold omelette over to enclose
filling, then cut in half.
3 Spread toast with cheese; serve with omelette.

Sarah's diary
*Managed to get my belt in an
extra notch this morning; the
diet is obviously working! I
have so much basil in the
garden at the moment, I
decided to throw a bit into
the spinach omelette for
breakfast. Such a great,
fresh flavour. Lunch was
yum – I can't remember the
last time I had turkey and
cranberry. Had a friend's
birthday dinner, so had to
miss the diet dinner. After
scanning the menu at the
Asian restaurant for a
healthy option, I went for the
steamed vegie dumplings –
they certainly hit the spot.*

Pamela's diary
*Sarah has the tiniest waist
of anyone I've ever known,
and it's getting tinier, she
looks terrific. We both agree
this diet is really good, easy
to follow, well-balanced,
with a wide variety of
food and, for those of us
watching the budget, and
who isn't these days, it's
quite inexpensive. We've
deliberately avoided exotic
ingredients, we bought
everything we needed from
mainstream supermarkets.*

Save the egg yolks by freezing them in ice block trays and use for making something decadent after the diet. Don't be afraid to turn the heat up high when you're cooking the omelette; fast and hot is the way to go.

Pea shoots are often hard to get. Substitute with bean sprouts. By all means, use rocket, or any left-over greens instead of the spinach. These wraps travel well; make them the night before, if you like.

LUNCH

turkey and cranberry wrap

preparation time 5 minutes **serves** 2
nutritional count per serving 2.1g total fat
(0.4g saturated fat); 849kJ (203 cal);
27.6g carbohydrate; 16.7g protein; 2.5g fibre

2 wholemeal wraps (60g)
2 tablespoons cranberry sauce
80g shaved turkey
30g pea shoots
30g baby spinach leaves

1 Spread wraps with sauce; top with remaining ingredients. Roll to enclose.

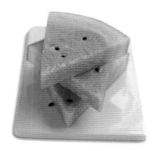

snack 200g watermelon

prosciutto-wrapped lamb with roasted potatoes

preparation time 15 minutes
cooking time 30 minutes **serves** 2
nutritional count per serving 7.3g total fat
(3.3g saturated fat); 1488kJ (356 cal);
33.7g carbohydrate; 34.8g protein; 7.3g fibre

The ruby red grapefruit is lovely in this recipe, but you could use orange segments. Don't bother to peel the potatoes, the skin is good for you.

400g potatoes, halved lengthways
200g lamb fillet
1 clove garlic, sliced finely
2 slices prosciutto (30g)
150g green beans, trimmed
1 ruby red grapefruit (350g), segmented
¼ cup coarsely chopped fresh flat-leaf parsley
30g reduced-fat fetta cheese, crumbled

1 Preheat oven to 220°C/200°C fan-forced.
2 Place potato in small ovenproof dish; roast, uncovered, 15 minutes.
3 Meanwhile, cut small slits in lamb; fill each slit with a garlic slice. Wrap prosciutto around lamb. Cook lamb in heated medium frying pan, 1 minute each side. Remove from pan; place on top of potato.
4 Roast lamb and potato, uncovered, about 10 minutes.
5 Meanwhile, boil, steam or microwave beans until tender.
6 Combine beans with remaining ingredients in medium bowl.
7 Slice lamb, serve with potato and salad.

snack 2 kiwifruit

Day 10 Menu

ricotta and banana on toast | beef, mint and cucumber salad | cumin fish with roasted corn salsa

ricotta and banana on toast

preparation time 5 minutes **serves** 2
nutritional count per serving 3.5g total fat
(1.6g saturated fat); 970kJ (232 cal);
40.6g carbohydrate; 7.7g protein; 5.0g fibre

2 tablespoons ricotta cheese
2 slices rye bread (90g), toasted
2 small bananas (260g), sliced thickly
1 teaspoon honey
pinch ground cinnamon

1 Divide cheese between slices of toast; top with banana, drizzle with honey, then sprinkle with cinnamon.

Sarah's diary
I've lost 2.3kg and I feel good. Breakfast felt like a real treat; I love banana and cinnamon. Pamela and I both enjoyed lunch – it was so filling. Shops had sold out of red capsicum, so I had to use cherry tomatoes in the salsa for dinner instead, and it worked just fine. The testing for the chocolate cookbook continued today… truffles galore – usually I would've devoured a whole tray, but I was very pleased with my restraint and only had a crumb.

Pamela's diary
Felt a bit on the greedy side today; there seemed to be more food than on other days. When we first tested the recipes for this diet, we were tasting the meals for a whole day all at the one time, so we decided that there really was only one way to test the diet properly, and that was to do it over the full three weeks. We always knew that we would be interrupted by tastings for other cookbooks and various family functions, but we figured, that's life.

If you're taking this salad to work, hold the lemon juice until you're ready to eat. Otherwise, eat the salad while the beef is still warm.

beef, mint and cucumber salad

200g rump steak
cooking-oil spray
300g can chickpeas, rinsed, drained
½ cucumber (130g), chopped coarsely
2 small tomatoes (180g), chopped coarsely
½ small red onion (50g), sliced thinly
⅓ cup coarsely chopped fresh mint
¼ cup (60ml) lemon juice

1 Spray beef with cooking oil. Cook beef in heated small frying pan; remove from heat. Cover; stand 5 minutes.
2 Slice beef thinly; combine with remaining ingredients in medium bowl.

preparation time 10 minutes (plus standing time)
cooking time 5 minutes **serves** 2
nutritional count per serving 6.0g total fat
(1.5g saturated fat); 1145kJ (274 cal);
19.2g carbohydrate; 31.7g protein; 7.5g fibre

snack 1 small
red capsicum with
1 tablespoon low-fat
cottage cheese

If limes are too expensive,
use lemons instead.
Any firm white fish is good
for this recipe.

snack 1 small pear

DINNER

cumin fish with roasted corn salsa

2 trimmed corn cobs (500g)
⅓ cup coarsely chopped fresh coriander
1 small red capsicum (150g), chopped finely
3 green onions, chopped finely
2 tablespoons lime juice
300g firm white fish fillets
1 teaspoon ground cumin

preparation time 10 minutes
cooking time 10 minutes **serves** 2
nutritional count per serving 5.7g total fat
(1.2g saturated fat); 1534kJ (367 cal);
33.6g carbohydrate; 39.9g protein; 9.5g fibre

1 Cut kernels from corn cobs; roast corn in heated medium frying pan, stirring constantly. Transfer to medium bowl.
2 Stir in coriander, capsicum, onion and juice.
3 Sprinkle fish with cumin; cook in same heated pan.
4 Serve corn salsa topped with fish. Serve with lime wedges, if you like.

Day 11 Menu

watermelon, raspberry and cranberry salad | chicken waldorf salad | beef rissoles with beetroot salad

watermelon, raspberry and cranberry salad

preparation time 5 minutes **serves** 2
nutritional count per serving 0.9g total fat
(0.1g saturated fat); 757kJ (181 cal);
33.6g carbohydrate; 6.7g protein; 5.0g fibre

400g watermelon, cut into 2cm pieces
1 cup (135g) fresh raspberries
½ cup (125ml) diet cranberry juice
1 tablespoon coarsely chopped fresh mint
¾ cup (200g) skim-milk fruit-flavoured yogurt

1 Combine fruit, juice and mint in medium bowl.
Serve topped with yogurt.

Sarah's diary
Went for a swim this morning; a refreshing way to start the day (and quite refreshing that my bikini fitted quite well!). I found breakfast quite light, but loved the watermelon and raspberries. Had tastings all morning for the Cooking from the Pantry cookbook – goodness me, the teaspoon I had of the chorizo & pumpkin risotto was so delicious, I could've eaten the entire bowl. Waldorf for lunch was nice; I didn't think the diet version would be good, but it surprised me. Dinner hit the spot; gotta love a rissole!

Pamela's diary
Well, we're half way through now, and despite the interruptions, we're both liking this diet, and are even thinking of doing it again. We're both looking better, sleeping well, are more energetic and feeling good. The tastings in the Test Kitchen are a great temptation, but we have been restrained so far, although we both nearly "cracked" over a very good risotto today. I just read Sarah's diary entry – am glad I didn't have to beach-test a bikini.

Strawberries are a good, and cheaper, substitute for raspberries. Match the yogurt flavour to your choice of berries.

preparation time 10 minutes (plus cooling time)
cooking time 10 minutes **serves** 2
nutritional count per serving 2.7g total fat
(0.6g saturated fat); 761kJ (182 cal);
11.0g carbohydrate; 26.1g protein; 4.1g fibre

If you're taking this salad to work, make sure the apple is coated with the dressing to stop the flesh discolouring.

snack 1 small carrot

LUNCH

chicken waldorf salad

2 cups (500ml) water
200g chicken breast fillet
¼ cup (70g) skim-milk natural yogurt
2 tablespoons lemon juice
1 teaspoon wholegrain mustard
1 small red apple (130g), sliced thinly
3 trimmed celery stalks (300g), sliced diagonally
2 tablespoons coarsely chopped fresh flat-leaf parsley

1 Bring the water to the boil in a medium saucepan; add chicken. Simmer, covered, about 10 minutes or until chicken is cooked. Cool chicken in poaching liquid for 10 minutes; drain, then slice thickly.
2 Meanwhile, combine yogurt, juice and mustard in medium bowl. Add apple, celery, parsley and chicken; mix gently.

beef rissoles with beetroot salad

220g lean beef mince
1 clove garlic, crushed
2 teaspoons ground cumin
cooking-oil spray
200g baby beetroot, halved
⅓ cup coarsely chopped fresh flat-leaf parsley
3 green onions, sliced thinly
1 tablespoon balsamic vinegar
2 tablespoons low-fat cottage cheese

1 Combine beef, garlic and cumin in small bowl; shape mixture into four patties.
2 Spray medium frying pan with cooking oil; heat pan. Cook patties in pan.
3 Meanwhile, combine beetroot, parsley, onion and vinegar in medium bowl.
4 Serve salad topped with patties and dolloped with cheese.

snack 1 medium orange

preparation time 10 minutes
cooking time 10 minutes **serves** 2
nutritional count per serving 8.9g total fat (3.4g saturated fat); 949kJ (227 cal); 7.9g carbohydrate; 27.1g protein; 2.9g fibre

Day 12 Menu

muesli with pear and yogurt | egg and chive sandwich | ham, tomato and rocket pizza

muesli with pear and yogurt

preparation time 5 minutes **serves** 2
nutritional count per serving 1.8g total fat
(0.4g saturated fat); 896kJ (213 cal);
37.6g carbohydrate; 8.1g protein; 5.8g fibre

⅔ cup bran and cranberry muesli (see recipe, page 32)
1 small pear (180g), sliced thinly
½ cup (140g) skim-milk fruit-flavoured yogurt
⅓ cup (80ml) skim milk

1 Serve muesli topped with pear, then yogurt and milk.

Sarah's diary
Over half-way through and I'm really starting to notice the difference in how my clothes fit. Breakfast was quick to prepare and tasted great. We have a tradition in the Test Kitchen of having curried egg sandwiches once a fortnight for lunch, so today Pamela and I had our version of the egg sandwich, sans whole-egg mayo. I baby-sat the kids next door this evening, so we made the pizzas together – they were none the wiser that it was a lot healthier than the usual takeaway pizza.

Pamela's diary
We have this Test Kitchen thing for curried egg sandwiches; Sarah rallied with her own very acceptable version, it has the yum factor without the fat. I'm not much of a pizza fan, but I have to say the pizza tonight was very good, and as for that muesli, I love it – the trick is to not eat too much of it. If you're in a rush, or not into cooking breakfasts, especially during the week, remember, you can have this muesli for breakfast every day if you like.

This is the perfect portable lunch. Boil the eggs the night before and make the filling and the sandwiches in the morning. Wrap them well in plastic wrap. If you like, add in some curry powder to taste.

snack 2 corn thins with ½ small sliced tomato

LUNCH

egg and chive sandwich

preparation time 5 minutes **serves** 2
nutritional count per serving 9.6g total fat
(3.3g saturated fat); 1404kJ (336 cal);
40.6g carbohydrate; 19.2g protein; 6.2g fibre

2 hard-boiled eggs, halved
1 tablespoon ricotta cheese
2 tablespoons low-fat cottage cheese
2 tablespoons finely chopped fresh chives
4 slices rye bread (180g)

1 Place egg, cheeses and chives in medium bowl; using potato masher or back of fork, crush until combined.
2 Divide egg mixture between two slices of bread; top with remaining bread.

preparation time 10 minutes
cooking time 10 minutes serves 2
nutritional count per serving 9.2g total fat
(4.3g saturated fat); 1630kJ (390 cal);
43.3g carbohydrate; 27.1g protein; 8.4g fibre

ham, tomato and rocket pizza

2 large wholemeal pitta bread (160g)
2 tablespoons tomato paste
150g shaved ham
250g cherry tomatoes, halved
¼ small red onion (25g), sliced thinly
⅓ cup (80g) ricotta cheese
30g baby rocket leaves
2 tablespoons finely shredded fresh basil

1 Preheat oven to 200°C/180°C fan-forced.
2 Place bread on oven trays; spread with paste. Divide ham, tomato and onion between bread; top with dollops of cheese.
3 Bake about 10 minutes. Serve sprinkled with rocket and basil.

snack 1 small banana

Day 13 Menu

roasted mushrooms with ricotta | chicken and pumpkin curry | hoisin pork with watercress salad

roasted mushrooms with ricotta

preparation time 5 minutes
cooking time 15 minutes **serves** 2
nutritional count per serving 7.3g total fat
(4.3g saturated fat); 581kJ (139 cal);
3.8g carbohydrate; 12.4g protein; 4.7g fibre

4 flat mushrooms (320g)
½ cup (120g) ricotta cheese
2 tablespoons coarsely chopped fresh flat-leaf parsley
2 green onions, chopped finely
1 clove garlic, crushed

1 Preheat oven to 200°C/180°C fan-forced.
2 Place mushrooms, stem-side up, on oven tray.
Roast, uncovered, about 15 minutes.
3 Meanwhile, combine remaining ingredients in small bowl.
4 Serve mushrooms topped with cheese mixture.

Sarah's diary
Determined not to break the discipline on the weekend, my boyfriend and I had breakfast at home before going out for a coffee and newspaper read-a-thon. No complaints about the mushrooms – very filling. We had lunch quite late, but the curry didn't take long at all to make, and was satisfying. Met friends at the beach for late afternoon drinks; I settled for a small glass of wine. Had a friend's birthday bash at 8pm, so ate dinner just before I left home, which stopped me from tucking into the hummus!

Pamela's diary
It's so easy to be slack on the weekends with diets, but we are both so inspired by this diet that we're determined to follow it as best we can. By now you'll have noticed that you eat quite a lot of dairy products in this diet, all low-fat, of course, and tomatoes feature quite a lot also. We've been quite strict about ensuring the correct balance of fruit, vegies, protein, dairy foods and carbs, etc.

Try these mushrooms cooked on a
barbecue, they make a great breakfast for
lots of people – let your friends dollop their
own cheese mix onto the mushrooms.

Brown rice takes about 30 minutes to cook, sometimes less depending on how crunchy you like it.
If you want takeaway curry, the whole recipe can be made a day ahead, then reheated in a microwave oven at lunch time.

LUNCH

chicken and pumpkin curry

preparation time 15 minutes
cooking time 30 minutes **serves** 2
nutritional count per serving 8.7g total fat (4.6g saturated fat); 1973kJ (472 cal); 60.8g carbohydrate; 32.7g protein; 8.3g fibre

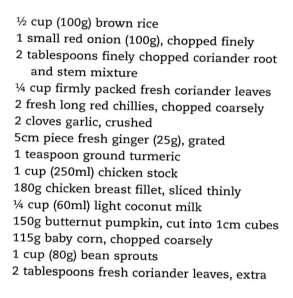

½ cup (100g) brown rice
1 small red onion (100g), chopped finely
2 tablespoons finely chopped coriander root and stem mixture
¼ cup firmly packed fresh coriander leaves
2 fresh long red chillies, chopped coarsely
2 cloves garlic, crushed
5cm piece fresh ginger (25g), grated
1 teaspoon ground turmeric
1 cup (250ml) chicken stock
180g chicken breast fillet, sliced thinly
¼ cup (60ml) light coconut milk
150g butternut pumpkin, cut into 1cm cubes
115g baby corn, chopped coarsely
1 cup (80g) bean sprouts
2 tablespoons fresh coriander leaves, extra

1 Cook rice in large saucepan of boiling water until tender; drain.
2 Meanwhile, blend onion, coriander root and stem mixture, coriander leaves, chilli, garlic, ginger and turmeric until smooth.
3 Cook paste in medium frying pan, stirring, until fragrant. Add stock, chicken and coconut milk; bring to a boil. Reduce heat; simmer, covered, 10 minutes.
4 Add pumpkin and corn to pan; simmer, uncovered, 10 minutes.
5 Serve rice topped with curry, sprouts and extra coriander.

snack 125g strawberries

Watercress is a wonderful vegetable full of goodies like vitamins A, C and E, and is very high in iron and folic acid. It's a bit time-consuming to handle, as you need to pick off the sprigs, then wash and dry them carefully. We think it's worth the effort, but you can use spinach leaves instead, if you like.

DINNER

hoisin pork with watercress salad

preparation time 15 minutes (plus standing time)
cooking time 10 minutes **serves** 2
nutritional count per serving 4.7g total fat
(1.2g saturated fat); 1066kJ (255 cal);
16.7g carbohydrate; 32.3g protein; 8.1g fibre

250g pork fillet
2 tablespoons hoisin sauce
cooking-oil spray
350g watercress, trimmed
⅓ cup coarsely chopped fresh mint
1 small green apple (130g), sliced thinly
½ small red onion (50g), sliced thinly
2 tablespoons lime juice
1 tablespoon light soy sauce
2cm piece fresh ginger (10g), grated
1 fresh small red thai chilli, chopped finely

1 Spread pork with hoisin sauce. Spray medium frying pan with cooking oil; heat pan, cook pork. Cover pork; stand 5 minutes.
2 Meanwhile, combine watercress, mint, apple and onion in medium bowl.
3 Combine juice, soy sauce, ginger and chilli in small jug. Add to salad; toss to combine.
4 Serve salad topped with sliced pork.

snack 125g grapes

Day 14 Menu

scrambled eggs with asparagus | thai-flavoured prawn salad | beef with sweet potato wedges

scrambled eggs with asparagus

preparation time 5 minutes
cooking time 10 minutes **serves** 2
nutritional count per serving 6.4g total fat
(1.7g saturated fat); 518kJ (124 cal);
3.0g carbohydrate; 13.0g protein; 1.6g fibre

170g asparagus, trimmed
cooking-oil spray
2 eggs
2 egg whites
2 tablespoons skim milk
1 small tomato (90g), chopped finely
2 tablespoons coarsely chopped fresh flat-leaf parsley

1 Boil, steam or microwave asparagus until tender; drain
2 Meanwhile, spray medium frying pan with cooking oil. Whisk eggs, egg whites and milk in medium jug. Cook egg mixture in pan, over low heat, stirring, until almost set.
3 Serve asparagus and scrambled eggs sprinkled with tomato and parsley.

Sarah's diary
So nice to wake up this morning feeling good; had breakfast then did a bit of window shopping – saw a couple of things I'd like to try on after I finish the diet. Went to the seafood markets for lunch, so instead of the prawn salad, I had sushi. We had a barbecue on Sunday night, so I cooked my steak on the barbecue, too – I think everyone wanted to eat my wedges, but I wasn't about to share. I didn't feel like the peppercorn sauce or broccolini with my steak, so just had a bit of rocket and tomato on the side, instead.

Pamela's diary
Sunday was a bit of a disaster for me diet-wise; my family had a small gathering and, naturally enough for us, there was quite a lot of good food, good wine and fun involved. You could say I fell off the wagon, but there's always tomorrow and I've lost just over four kilos now. I wonder how long before Sunday's over-indulgences show up on the scales.

Scrambled eggs need to be cooked and stirred gently until they are creamy and barely cooked. Over-cooking will toughen them. Eat them straight away or they'll become watery.

This is a perfect lunch to take to work: get all the ingredients ready the night before, then assemble the salad in the morning. It must be covered and refrigerated.

snack 2 passionfruit

thai-flavoured prawn salad

preparation time 30 minutes (plus cooling time)
cooking time 25 minutes **serves** 2
nutritional count per serving 2.3g total fat
(0.4g saturated fat); 1492kJ (357 cal);
61.1g carbohydrate; 19.5g protein; 4.6g fibre

¾ cup (150g) brown rice
250g cooked small prawns, shelled, deveined
1 small carrot (70g), grated coarsely
3 green onions, chopped finely
2 tablespoons coarsely chopped fresh coriander
1 clove garlic, crushed
1 teaspoon finely grated lime rind
¼ cup (60ml) lime juice
1 fresh small red thai chilli, chopped finely

1 Cook rice in large saucepan of boiling water, uncovered, until tender; drain, cool.
2 Combine rice in large bowl with remaining ingredients.

preparation time 5 minutes
cooking time 25 minutes serves 2
nutritional count per serving 7.0g total fat
(2.5g saturated fat); 1367kJ (327 cal);
26.7g carbohydrate; 35.4g protein; 6.7g fibre

If you don't like green peppercorns, leave them out, and just season the steak with freshly ground black pepper.

beef with sweet potato wedges

1 medium sweet potato (400g), cut into wedges
175g tenderstem broccoli
2 beef fillet steaks (250g)
cooking-oil spray
1 tablespoon drained green peppercorns
1 tablespoon buttermilk
½ cup (125ml) beef stock

1 Preheat oven to 200°C/180°C fan-forced.
2 Roast sweet potato on oven tray, uncovered, about
25 minutes. Boil, steam or microwave broccolini until tender.
3 Meanwhile, spray beef with cooking oil; cook beef in
heated medium frying pan. Remove from heat;
cover with foil.
4 Add peppercorns, buttermilk and stock to pan; heat
without boiling.
5 Serve vegetables topped with beef, then drizzled with
peppercorn sauce.

snack 100g skim-milk
fruit-flavoured yogurt

Day 15 Menu

citrus salad | tuna, celery and dill sandwich | grilled mustard-chicken with potato smash

citrus salad

preparation time 15 minutes **serves** 2
nutritional count per serving 0.7g total fat
(0.1g saturated fat); 911kJ (218 cal);
40.6g carbohydrate; 8.9g protein; 5.4g fibre

1 medium pink grapefruit (425g), segmented
2 medium navel oranges (480g), segmented
1 lime, segmented
60g strawberries, quartered
½ cup (125ml) unsweetened apple juice
¾ cup (200g) skim-milk fruit-flavoured yogurt

1 Combine fruit and juice in medium bowl. Serve topped with yogurt.

Sarah's diary
I remember when we were really young, Mum always gave us grapefruit with our breakfast, but we would only eat it after it had been covered in about 10 spoons of sugar. Those days have gone, because I thoroughly enjoyed my fruit salad without any added sugar. Was starving by lunchtime and the sandwich hit the spot. Made my housemates dinner as well tonight – they claimed that it looked and tasted like "restaurant food". Well, if that's what they thought, then this diet can't be too bad!

Pamela's diary
Fruit for breakfast is my favourite, it certainly is the lightest and cleanest food to start the day with, especially in the summer months. Mondays are usually a bit spartan in the Test Kitchen in terms of tastings, which is probably a good thing after yesterday, so, I'm back on the wagon and feeling happy about it. Loved the corn and potato smash for dinner.

If you can't find pink (or ruby) grapefruit, use the ordinary grapefruit. Any combination of citrus fruit is fine; mix and match to suit your tastes.

tuna, celery and dill sandwich

preparation time 10 minutes **serves** 2
nutritional count per serving 6.5g total fat
(2.5g saturated fat); 1534kJ (367 cal);
42.8g carbohydrate; 29.8g protein; 8g fibre

185g can tuna in springwater, drained, flaked
2 trimmed celery stalks (200g), chopped finely
¼ small red onion (25g), chopped finely
2 tablespoons ricotta cheese
1 tablespoon coarsely chopped fresh dill
2 teaspoons rinsed, drained baby capers
4 slices rye bread (180g)
20g baby spinach leaves

1 Combine tuna, celery, onion, cheese, dill and capers
in medium bowl.
2 Divide spinach between two bread slices; top with
tuna mixture, then remaining bread.

If you're taking this
sandwich to work, make
the filling the night before,
then make the sandwich
in the morning. Put it in
the fridge when you arrive
at work. The spinach (or try
cos lettuce) will stop the
bread from turning soggy.

snack 125g grape tomatoes

snack 1 small apple

grilled mustard-chicken with potato smash

preparation time 15 minutes
cooking time 15 minutes **serves** 2
nutritional count per serving 5.7g total fat
(1.0g saturated fat); 2057kJ (492 cal);
62.6g carbohydrate; 41.3g protein; 10.8g fibre

3 medium potatoes (600g), unpeeled, halved
260g chicken breast fillet
cooking-oil spray
2 teaspoons wholegrain mustard
310g can corn kernels, rinsed, drained
2 tablespoons skim milk
2 tablespoons finely chopped fresh chives
1 lemon

1 Boil, steam or microwave potato until tender; drain.
2 Meanwhile, spray chicken with cooking oil; cook chicken on heated grill plate (or grill or barbecue), brushing occasionally with mustard. Cover chicken; stand 5 minutes, then slice thickly.
3 Combine potato, corn, milk and chives in large bowl; use potato masher or back of fork to crush mixture.
4 Serve chicken with potato smash and lemon wedges.

Day 16 Menu

banana passionfruit smoothie | caesar salad | moussaka stack with lemon-yogurt dressing

banana passionfruit smoothie

preparation time 5 minutes **serves** 2
nutritional count per serving 0.5g total fat
(0.2g saturated fat); 1628kJ (246 cal);
46.0g carbohydrate; 12.2g protein; 2.9g fibre

2 medium bananas (400g)
1 cup (250ml) skim milk
¾ cup (200g) skim-milk passionfruit-flavoured yogurt
Pinch ground nutmeg

1 Blend bananas, milk and yogurt until smooth.
Serve smoothies lightly sprinked with nutmeg.

Sarah's diary
Nearly 3.5kg lost to date – I really can't believe it. I haven't felt this good in a long time. My sugar cravings have been well and truly put to rest, finally! The smoothie was good; I froze my banana last night so I had a super-icy breakfast. The caesar salad was nice. I'm not usually a big fan of caesar salads but I actually enjoyed this one. Dinner was definitely my fave so far in this whole diet...couldn't believe it was diet food.

Pamela's diary
Sarah looks wonderful; we both agree this diet is the best-ever, and let me tell you, between us we've probably tried every diet known to mankind, so we know what we're talking about. This diet was originally devised by home economist Amanda Lennon, but Sarah and I have tweaked the recipes as we've been going along; it's been very much a diet in progress, so much so that we've resolved to do it again. What's to lose, only more weight.

We liked the flavour combination of passionfruit and banana, but any flavoured yogurt of your choice is fine. Bananas are at their sweetest when ripe, but slightly underripe bananas will make your digestive system work harder – so burning more calories.

If you don't feel like toasting the bread cubes in the oven, toast the whole slices in the toaster or under a grill then cut the bread into small squares. Make sure you drain the anchovy fillet well between pieces of absorbent paper. If you want to have this delicious recipe at home, poach the egg instead of boiling it. Hold the yogurt dressing until you're ready to eat.

caesar salad

preparation time 10 minutes
cooking time 5 minutes **serves** 2
nutritional count per serving 5.6g total fat (1.4g saturated fat); 991kJ (237 cal); 25.7g carbohydrate; 17.1g protein; 6.9g fibre

2 slices rye bread (90g)
2 slices prosciutto (30g)
¼ cup (70g) skim-milk natural yogurt
1 tablespoon lemon juice
1 well-drained anchovy fillet, chopped finely
1 teaspoon dijon mustard
2 baby cos lettuces, trimmed, leaves separated
1 hard-boiled egg, sliced thinly

1 Preheat oven to 180°C/160°C fan-forced.
2 Remove crusts from bread; cut bread into small squares. Place on oven tray; toast about 5 minutes.
3 Meanwhile, cook prosciutto in medium heated frying pan until crisp; chop coarsely.
4 Combine yogurt, juice, anchovy and mustard in medium bowl. Add lettuce; toss to combine.
5 Serve lettuce mixture topped with toast, prosciutto and egg.

snack ½ cucumber with
1 tablespoon low-fat cottage cheese

moussaka stack with lemon-yogurt dressing

preparation time 15 minutes
cooking time 15 minutes **serves** 2
nutritional count per serving 6.9g total fat
(2.6g saturated fat); 957kJ (229 cal);
13.5g carbohydrate; 24.9g protein; 6.5g fibre

Substitute baby spinach leaves
for the rocket, if you wish.

snack 1 medium orange

1 small brown onion (80g), chopped finely
1 clove garlic, crushed
1 tablespoon beef stock
170g lean beef mince
2 small tomatoes (180g), chopped coarsely
¼ teaspoon ground cinnamon
¼ teaspoon ground nutmeg
½ cup (125ml) beef stock, extra
2 tablespoons coarsely chopped fresh flat-leaf parsley
2 tablespoons coarsely chopped fresh basil
1 medium eggplant (300g)
1 small red capsicum (150g), quartered
¼ cup (70g) skim-milk natural yogurt
2 teaspoons finely grated lemon rind
1 tablespoon lemon juice
20g baby rocket leaves

1 Cook onion, garlic and the beef stock in medium frying
pan until onion softens. Add beef, tomato and spices; cook,
stirring, until beef is browned. Add extra stock; bring to the
boil. Reduce heat; simmer, uncovered, about 5 minutes or
until liquid is absorbed. Remove from heat; stir in herbs.
2 Meanwhile, slice eggplant lengthways into 6 slices;
discard the two outside pieces. Cook eggplant and
capsicum on heated grill plate (or grill or barbecue)
until browned and tender.
3 Combine yogurt, rind and juice in small jug.
4 Stack beef mixture, eggplant, capsicum and rocket
on plates; drizzle with the yogurt mixture.

Day 17 Menu

cranberry and apple muesli | salmon pasta salad | sweet chilli chicken salad

cranberry and apple muesli

preparation time 5 minutes
(plus refrigeration time) **serves** 2
nutritional count per serving 3.2g total fat
(0.6g saturated fat); 1133kJ (271 cal);
48.1g carbohydrate; 9.9g protein; 4.1g fibre

¾ cup (200g) skim-milk natural yogurt
¾ cup (65g) rolled oats
⅓ cup (80ml) unsweetened apple juice
1 small green apple (130g), grated coarsely
¼ cup (35g) dried cranberries

1 Combine yogurt, oats and juice in small bowl;
cover, refrigerate 3 hours or overnight.
2 Just before serving, stir in remaining ingredients.

Sarah's diary
*Was great to get up this
morning and just pull
breakfast straight from
the fridge – the joys of
preparing it the night before!
Muesli is one of my all-time
favourites, and this one
did not disappoint. Wasn't
actually that hungry at
lunchtime, and just picked
at the salad. Made dinner
for a couple of friends, and
everyone really enjoyed the
salad – I wouldn't mind
taking some to work for
lunch one day.*

Pamela's diary
*So far, I've lost more weight
than Sarah, the sad truth
is, I had more to lose. Sarah
has been more diligent with
exercise than me during
this diet, maybe she has
developed muscle, whereas
there's very little chance of
that happening to me. I love
to walk, but by nature, I'm
not one to push myself.
However, now that I'm
feeling more energetic due
to the weight loss, I'm up in
the morning, and walking
more and faster than before.*

It's not vital that you soak the oats
overnight, but it's preferable.
Cranberries are rich in anti-oxidants,
but if you like, substitute sultanas.

Choose any pasta you like for this delicious salad. You could make it the night before, if you like. Keep it in the fridge.

snack 2 cups plain popcorn (see page 52)

preparation time 10 minutes
cooking time 10 minutes **serves** 2
nutritional count per serving 9.1g total fat
(3.3g saturated fat); 1919kJ (459 cal);
56.4g carbohydrate; 32.3g protein; 5.1g fibre

LUNCH

salmon pasta salad

1 cup (150g) spiral pasta
170g asparagus, trimmed, chopped coarsely
2 tablespoons ricotta cheese
1 teaspoon finely grated lemon rind
¼ cup (60ml) lemon juice
1 clove garlic, crushed
1 small red capsicum (150g), sliced thinly
⅓ cup coarsely chopped fresh flat-leaf parsley
2 green onions, sliced thinly
210g can pink salmon in springwater, drained, flaked

1   Cook pasta in medium saucepan of boiling water, uncovered, until just tender. Add asparagus; cook 1 minute. Drain.
2   Meanwhile, combine cheese, rind, juice and garlic in large bowl; add pasta, asparagus and remaining ingredients to bowl; toss to combine.

sweet chilli chicken salad

2 cups (500ml) water
200g chicken breast fillet
1¼ cups (100g) bean sprouts
1 small red capsicum (150g), sliced thinly
1 small carrot (70g), cut into matchsticks
1 fresh long red chilli, sliced thinly
⅓ cup firmly packed fresh coriander leaves
3cm piece fresh ginger (15g), cut into matchsticks
¼ cup (60ml) lime juice
1 tablespoon sweet chilli sauce
2 teaspoons fish sauce

1 Bring water to the boil in medium saucepan; add chicken. Simmer, covered, about 10 minutes or until chicken is cooked. Cool chicken in poaching liquid 10 minutes; drain, shred coarsely.
2 Combine chicken in medium bowl with sprouts, capsicum, carrot, chilli, coriander and ginger.
3 Shake juice and sauces together in screw-top jar, drizzle over salad.

snack 200g rockmelon

preparation time 15 minutes
cooking time 10 minutes **serves** 2
nutritional count per serving 2.9g total fat (0.6g saturated fat); 727kJ (174 cal); 8.2g carbohydrate; 26.5g protein; 4.2g fibre

Add a finely chopped fresh red thai chilli if you want to heat up this salad.

Day 18 Menu

brekky beans | tuna tabbouleh | beef skewers with greek salad

brekky beans

preparation time 10 minutes
cooking time 10 minutes **serves** 2
nutritional count per serving 2.8g total fat
(0.5g saturated fat); 1241kJ (297 cal);
43.3g carbohydrate; 17.3g protein; 13.4g fibre

1 small brown onion (80g), chopped finely
1 clove garlic, crushed
2 back bacon rashers (30g), chopped finely
400g can diced tomatoes
1 tablespoon tomato paste
1 tablespoon wholegrain mustard
400g can white beans, rinsed, drained
2 tablespoons coarsely chopped fresh flat-leaf parsley
2 slices rye bread (90g), toasted

1 Cook onion, garlic and bacon in heated medium saucepan until onion softens. Add undrained tomatoes, paste and mustard; cook, stirring, until hot. Add beans; cook, stirring, until hot. Stir in parsley.
2 Serve bean mixture with toast.

Sarah's diary
I can't believe the diet finishes on Sunday – time has flown. I'm really looking forward to weighing myself at the end. Loved breakfast this morning, I think it's becoming quite obvious what my favourite meal of the day is! Had to eat lunch in a flash because we were so busy, thankfully it was just a light salad, but still delicious.

Pamela's diary
Loved the beans for breakfast, they're so good for the digestive system. Lots of tastings today, both sweet and savoury: it's hard to walk away from food that you really like, but we do keep an eye on each other, which helps. I had to go to a lunch for work today – had to eat three courses, and drank a glass (or was it two?) of Champagne... oh well, someone has to do it.

Back bacon is the largest, and
leanest, end of a bacon rasher.
Any canned white bean can be
used; we like cannelini beans.

snack 2 kiwifruit

LUNCH

tuna tabbouleh

preparation time 10 minutes **serves** 2
nutritional count per serving 2.4g total fat
(0.8g saturated fat); 920kJ (220 cal);
23.4g carbohydrate; 24.0g protein; 3.2g fibre

¼ cup (50g) couscous
¼ cup (60ml) boiling water
185g can tuna in springwater, drained, flaked
½ cup finely chopped fresh flat-leaf parsley
3 small tomatoes (270g), seeded, chopped finely
3 green onions, sliced thinly
¼ cup (60ml) lemon juice
1 clove garlic, crushed

1 Combine couscous with the water in medium heatproof
bowl, cover; stand 5 minutes or until water is absorbed.
Mix in remaining ingredients.

Make the salad the night
before, or in the morning
and keep it in the fridge.

preparation time 15 minutes
cooking time 10 minutes **serves** 2
nutritional count per serving 5.4g total fat
(1.8g saturated fat); 1020kJ (244 cal);
8.7g carbohydrate; 37.8g protein; 4.0g fibre

DINNER

beef skewers with greek salad

300g rump steak, cut into 2cm cubes
1 tablespoon finely chopped fresh thyme
cooking-oil spray
2 small tomatoes (190g), chopped coarsely
1 small green capsicum (150g), chopped coarsely
¼ cup (30g) seeded black olives
½ cucumber (130g), chopped coarsely
¼ cup coarsely chopped fresh flat-leaf parsley
1 lemon

1 Combine beef and thyme in medium bowl; thread
beef onto skewers. Spray beef with cooking oil; cook
skewers on heated grill plate (or grill or barbecue).
2 Meanwhile, combine remaining ingredients in
medium bowl.
3 Serve salad with beef skewers and lemon wedges.

You need to soak four bamboo
skewers in cold water for at least
10 minutes before using to prevent
them scorching during cooking. If
you think of it, overnight soaking
of the bamboo skewers is even
better. You can, of course, use
metal skewers, if you prefer.

snack 1 small pear

Day 19 Menu

breakfast fry-up | chicken and bacon club | cajun fish with rice pilaf

breakfast fry-up

preparation time 5 minutes
cooking time 10 minutes· **serves** 2
nutritional count per serving 1.5g total fat
(0.1g saturated fat); 652kJ (156 cal);
22.5g carbohydrate; 8.9g protein; 7.6g fibre

2 small tomatoes (180g), quartered
1 tablespoon balsamic vinegar
150g mushrooms, sliced thickly
100g baby spinach leaves
2 tablespoons coarsely chopped fresh basil
2 slices rye bread (90g), toasted

1 Preheat oven to 220°C/200°C fan-forced.
2 Combine tomato and half the vinegar in small shallow baking dish. Roast, uncovered, about 10 minutes.
3 Meanwhile, cook mushrooms, spinach and remaining vinegar in large frying pan until mushroom is tender and spinach wilts; stir in basil.
4 Serve tomato and mushroom mixture on toast.

It's worth buying the best, most flavoursome tomatoes you can. We use a balsamic vinegar bought from the supermarket, but if you're lucky enough to have a first-grade balsamic vinegar, use it sparingly, as you might only need 1 teaspoon instead of 1 tablespoon.

Sarah's diary
Bought a pair of jeans last night, was very exciting – haven't been brave enough to go shopping for jeans for about 3 years. Was super-rushed this morning, so I just had a bowl of the bran & cranberry muesli from Day 4 for breakfast – an easy solution if you're running short of time. The dinner was especially yummy, haven't had pilaf in a long time and it was delicious.

Pamela's diary
Never seen Sarah in jeans before, she looks great, positively leggy. Today's meals were particularly scrumptious; the fry-up seemed decadent, but the fat count has been carefully calculated, you could fool anyone into believing that this is not a diet breakfast. The club sandwich was wonderful, not to mention the fish with a pilaf, oh joy.

snack 125g grapes

This sandwich is at its best eaten warm, but if you don't have the right facilities to cook the chicken and bacon at lunch time, then cook the chicken and bacon in the morning and assemble the sandwich at work.

LUNCH

chicken and bacon club

100g chicken breast fillet
cooking-oil spray
2 back bacon rashers (30g)
⅓ cup (65g) low-fat cottage cheese
4 slices rye bread (180g), toasted
20g baby rocket leaves
1 small tomato (90g), sliced thinly

1 Spray chicken with cooking oil; heat medium frying pan, cook chicken. Cover chicken; stand 5 minutes, then slice thinly.
2 Cook bacon in same pan until crisp.
3 Divide half the cheese between two toast slices; top with rocket, tomato, chicken, bacon, remaining cheese and toast.

preparation time 10 minutes
cooking time 8 minutes **serves** 2
nutritional count per serving 5.6g total fat
(1.2g saturated fat); 1459kJ (349 cal);
41.5g carbohydrate; 29.1g protein; 6.8g fibre

Choose any white firm-flesh fish you like; a thick-cut fillet or steak will be best.

cajun fish with rice pilaf

cooking-oil spray
1 small brown onion (80g), chopped finely
2 trimmed celery stalks (200g), chopped finely
2 cloves garlic, crushed
¼ teaspoon ground cinnamon
2 cloves
¼ teaspoon ground turmeric
¾ cup (150g) white long-grain rice
2 cups (500ml) chicken stock
¼ cup finely chopped fresh flat-leaf parsley
2 x 180g firm white fish fillets
2 teaspoons cajun spice powder

1 Spray base of medium saucepan with cooking oil; cook onion, celery and garlic, stirring, 5 minutes. Add spices; cook, stirring, until fragrant. Add rice; stir to coat in mixture. Add stock; bring to the boil. Reduce heat; simmer, covered tightly, about 20 minutes or until rice is tender and liquid is absorbed. Stir in parsley.
2 Meanwhile, spray medium frying pan with cooking oil. Sprinkle fish with cajun spice; cook in pan.
3 Serve pilaf with fish.

snack 1 small apple

preparation time 10 minutes
cooking time 20 minutes serves 2
nutritional count per serving 6.6g total fat
(1.9g saturated fat); 2149kJ (514 cal);
64.7g carbohydrate; 46.0g protein; 3.8g fibre

Day 20 Menu

muesli muffins | tomato, zucchini and oregano slice | teriyaki chicken with noodles

preparation time 5 minutes
cooking time 25 minutes **makes** 6
nutritional count per muffin 9.1g total fat;
2.2g saturated fat; 1756kJ (420 cal);
64.7g carbohydrate; 16.2g protein; 5.7g fibre

muesli muffins

cooking-oil spray
½ cup bran and cranberry muesli (see recipe, page 32)
1 teaspoon vegetable oil
½ cup (140g) skim-milk natural yogurt
1 egg
⅔ cup (100g) self-raising flour
2 teaspoons finely grated orange rind
¼ teaspoon mixed spice
1 tablespoon demerara sugar
1 tablespoon ricotta cheese

1 Preheat oven to 180°C/160°C fan-forced. Spray six ⅓-cup (80ml) muffin pan holes with cooking oil, or line with paper cases.
2 Combine muesli, oil, yogurt, egg, flour, rind and spice in medium bowl, mix with fork.
3 Divide mixture among pan holes; sprinkle with sugar. Bake about 25 minutes.
4 Serve 2 muffins each with cheese.

Sarah's diary

Tomorrow is D-day! Goodness me…time flies when you're losing weight! The muffins were good for breakfast; I didn't have an orange so I used lemon rind instead. Oregano is my least-favourite herb but, surprisingly, I enjoyed lunch. Went out for dinner with friends; it was quite hard deciding what to have on the menu as nothing seemed particularly healthy…what can you do. To compensate for my potentially unhealthy meal, I didn't have any wine and didn't even look at the dessert menu.

Pamela's diary

The reason we decided to make this diet a 21-day diet was quite simple, one or two weeks didn't seem enough, and if we wanted to go on it again, the meals would have seemed repetitive, so, we decided three weeks was just right. Sometimes people diet because they want to lose a few kilos for an occasion, or to fit into a certain outfit, this diet would be ideal for that reason. But best of all, because it's not a crash diet, you won't look drawn or feel low in energy.

The muffins are suitable to freeze, stored in an
airtight container, for up to three months. Use raw
sugar instead of demerara if you like. Warm muffins
are best; they heat well in a microwave oven – about
20 seconds on HIGH (100%) will be enough.

snack 1 small pear

tomato, zucchini and oregano slice

preparation time 10 minutes
cooking time 35 minutes **serves** 2
nutritional count per serving 3.3g total fat
(1.1g saturated fat); 456kJ (109 cal);
3.1g carbohydrate; 15.7g protein; 2.1g fibre

This slice is great warm
or cold, and can be made
the night before. Keep the
slice in the fridge.

125g cherry tomatoes
1 egg
3 egg whites
⅓ cup (65g) low-fat cottage cheese
1 clove garlic, crushed
1 small zucchini (90g), grated coarsely
2 tablespoons coarsely chopped fresh oregano leaves
30g baby spinach leaves

1 Preheat oven to 200°C/180°C fan-forced. Line an
8cm x 21cm loaf pan with a strip of baking paper.
2 Place tomatoes in pan. Roast 10 minutes.
3 Meanwhile, combine egg, egg whites, cheese and
garlic in medium jug.
4 Remove tomatoes from oven; reduce oven temperature
to 160°C/140°C fan-forced.
5 Sprinkle tomatoes with zucchini and oregano; pour
over egg mixture. Bake about 25 minutes or until set.
6 Serve slice with spinach.

preparation time 10 minutes (plus refrigeration time)
cooking time 10 minutes **serves** 2
nutritional count per serving 4.3g total fat
(0.8g saturated fat); 1777kJ (425 cal);
59g carbohydrate; 33.7g protein; 5.2g fibre

DINNER

teriyaki chicken with noodles

160g chicken breast fillet, sliced thinly
⅓ cup (80ml) teriyaki sauce
1 clove garlic, crushed
cooking-oil spray
1 small red onion (100g), cut into wedges
⅓ cup (80ml) chicken stock
200g udon noodles
100g snow peas, halved lengthways
1 cup (80g) bean sprouts
1 fresh small red thai chilli, sliced thinly

1 Combine chicken, half the sauce and garlic in medium bowl; cover. Refrigerate 30 minutes.
2 Spray wok with cooking oil; cook chicken, in batches, in heated wok until browned.
3 Cook onion in wok 1 minute. Return chicken to wok with remaining sauce, stock, noodles and peas; stir-fry until hot.
4   Serve stir-fry topped with sprouts and chilli.

snack 125g strawberries

As with all stir-fries, do the preparation before you start to cook. If you don't like chilli, just leave it out.

Day 21 Menu

egg and bacon pies | chicken and pumpkin tortilla | honey-lemon prawn stir-fry

egg and bacon pies

preparation time 5 minutes
cooking time 15 minutes **serves** 2
nutritional count per serving 7.2g total fat
(2.0g saturated fat); 895kJ (214 cal);
21.0g carbohydrate; 21.0g protein; 3.6g fibre

2 back bacon rashers (30g), chopped finely
2 eggs
2 slices rye bread (90g), toasted
1 small tomato (90g), chopped finely

1 Preheat oven to 200°C/180°C fan-forced.
2 Divide bacon between two ⅓-cup (80ml) muffin pan holes. Crack an egg into each hole. Bake, about 15 minutes or until egg is set. Loosen edge of pies from pan.
3 Serves pies on toast, sprinkled with tomato.

Sarah's diary
5kg gone! And, it was sooooo easy. I feel fantastic – so fantastic, in fact, that Pamela and I are going to start the diet again tomorrow. Energised, inspired and fresh, I'm ready for another 21 days of good food…and weight loss, too.

Pamela's diary
Not that I'm gloating, but I've lost a whisker under six kilos in the last three weeks and, as I've told you, I've fallen off the diet several times. It is an easy diet to follow; the recipes are easy to make and have been devised to follow nutritional guidelines. It is essentially a low-fat diet, if you follow it, you WILL lose weight, there is no doubt about that. Give it a go, but remember to first check with your health practitioner if you have a medical condition.

Make the filling the night before, and fill the tortillas in the morning. If you have access to a sandwich press – heat the tortilla in the press.

chicken and pumpkin tortilla

preparation time 10 minutes
cooking time 10 minutes **serves** 2
nutritional count per serving 6.4g total fat (1.5g saturated fat); 1195kJ (286 cal); 26.1g carbohydrate; 29.1g protein; 3.0g fibre

160g chicken breast fillet
1 tablespoon taco seasoning mix
cooking-oil spray
150g butternut pumpkin, cut into 1cm cubes
2 tablespoons coarsely chopped fresh coriander
⅓ cup (65g) low-fat cottage cheese
2 green onions, chopped finely
2 tablespoons lime juice
1 clove garlic, crushed
2 x 15cm flour tortillas

1 Combine chicken and seasoning in small bowl.
2 Spray chicken with cooking oil; cook chicken, on one side, in heated medium frying pan 5 minutes. Turn chicken; add pumpkin. Cook chicken and pumpkin, uncovered, about 5 minutes or until both are cooked.
3 Chop chicken coarsely; combine in medium bowl with pumpkin and coriander.
4 Combine cheese, onion, juice and garlic in small bowl.
5 Spread cheese mixture, then chicken mixture on one tortilla; top with remaining tortilla. Serve cut into wedges.

snack muesli muffin (from day 20)

Have everything prepared before you start to cook. If you like, use brown rice instead of white.

honey-lemon prawn stir-fry

preparation time 15 minutes
cooking time 10 minutes **serves** 2
nutritional count per serving 2.1g total fat
(0.3g saturated fat); 1509kJ (361 cal);
43.8g carbohydrate; 38.6g protein; 4.1g fibre

⅓ cup (65g) white long-grain rice
1 teaspoon sesame seeds
650g uncooked king prawns, shelled,
    deveined, tails intact
1 small brown onion (80g), halved, cut into wedges
300g chinese cabbage, sliced thinly
1 small carrot (70g), cut into matchsticks
2 tablespoons lemon juice
1 tablespoon honey
2cm piece fresh ginger (10g), grated
2 green onions, sliced thinly

1 Cook rice in medium saucepan of boiling water, uncovered, until tender; drain.
2 Meanwhile, toast sesame seeds in heated wok; remove from wok.
3 Cook prawns in heated wok; remove.
4 Stir-fry brown onion in heated wok about 3 minutes or until tender. Return prawns to wok with chinese cabbage, carrot, juice, honey and ginger; stir-fry until hot.
5 Serve rice with stir-fry, sprinkled with sesame seeds and green onion.

snack 100g skim-milk
fruit-flavoured yogurt

Shopping List

STAPLES

PANTRY

1 can cooking-oil spray
Small bottle
  vegetable oil
Small bottle
  balsamic vinegar
Small jar fat-free
  mayonnaise
1 jar dijon mustard
1 jar wholegrain mustard
500ml beef stock
500ml vegetable stock
1 litre chicken stock
125g can four-bean mix
3 x 125g cans chickpeas
300g can chickpeas
400g can white beans
400g can brown lentils
3 x 310g cans corn kernels
5 x 185g cans tuna
  in springwater
210g can salmon
  in springwater
Small can anchovy fillets
2 x 400g cans
  diced tomatoes
Small tub tomato paste
Small can
  light coconut milk
Small bottle
  sweet chilli sauce
Small bottle fish sauce
Small bottle
  teriyaki sauce
Small bottle hoisin sauce
Small bottle oyster sauce
Small bottle
  light soy sauce
Small jar baby capers
Small jar cornichons
Small jar cranberry sauce
Small can green
  peppercorns
Small packet
  sesame seeds
Curry powder

Ground cumin
Dried chilli flakes
Sumac
Tandoori powder
Cajun spice powder
Ground fennel
Ground turmeric
Ground nutmeg
Ground cinnamon
Mixed spice
Whole cloves
Taco seasoning mix
Flour tortillas
Small packet small
  pappadams
Large packet brown rice
Small packet white
  long-grain rice
250g packet couscous
Small packet
  linguine pasta
Small packet spiral pasta
Small packet
  udon noodles (200g)
Small packet rolled oats
Small packet All Bran
Small packet white
  self-raising flour
Small packet wholemeal
  self-raising flour
Small packet brown sugar
Small packet
  demerara sugar
Small jar honey
Packet corn thins
Packet of popping corn
Small packet dried
  cranberries (need 80g)
Small packet dried dates
Small bottle diet
  cranberry juice

FREEZER

Small packet frozen
  baby peas

SHOPPING LIST WEEK 1

FRIDGE

5 x 100g tubs skim-milk
  fruit-flavoured yogurt
2 x 140g tubs skim-milk
  natural yogurt
1 x 200g carton ricotta
  cheese
1 x 200g tub low-fat
  cottage cheese
600ml carton buttermilk
600ml carton skim milk
12 eggs

FRUIT & VEG

600g rockmelon
200g honeydew melon
200g watermelon
1 medium mango
1 punnet blueberries
4 apricots, plums or
  kiwifruit
4 small apples
2 small bananas
250g grapes
5 lemons
2 limes
4 oranges
2 small pears
250g strawberries
5 small tomatoes
125g cherry tomatoes
125g yellow tear drop
  tomatoes
3 small red capsicums
1 fresh small
  red thai chilli
1 fresh long red chilli
1 bunch basil
1 bunch mint
2 bunches coriander
2 bunches flat-leaf parsley
160g baby spinach leaves
170g baby rocket
1 bunch green onions
1 bunch red radishes
  (300g)
150g snow peas

4 passionfruit
1 baby buk choy
170g asparagus
100g green beans
1 cucumber
¼ cabbage (80g)
4 small zucchinis (360g)
4 small carrots
2 flat mushrooms (160g)
200g butternut pumpkin
650g sweet potato
6 baby new potatoes (240g)
2 small brown onions
4 small red onions
1 bulb garlic
  (need 10 cloves)

MEAT & SEAFOOD

200g chicken breast fillet
280g chicken tenderloins
4 french-trimmed lamb
  cutlets (200g)
180g beef rump steak
2 pork cutlets (280g)
180g lean beef mince
320g white fish fillets
400g uncooked seafood
  mix
75g shaved ham
4 slices (120g) rare
  roast beef

MISCELLANEOUS

1 packet multi-grain
  english muffins
1 small loaf rye bread
1 packet wholemeal
  wraps

This comprehensive list covers every ingredient in the 21-day diet; most of the staples will be in your pantry already.

SHOPPING LIST WEEK 2

FRIDGE
8 x 100g tubs skim-milk
  fruit-flavoured yogurt
1 x 140g tub skim-milk
  natural yogurt
1 x 200g tub low-fat
  cottage cheese
2 x 200g cartons
  ricotta cheese
30g reduced-fat
  feta cheese
600ml carton skim milk
600ml carton buttermilk
12 eggs

FRUIT & VEG
800g watermelon
500g strawberries
75g blueberries
135g raspberries
1 ruby-red grapefruit
6 small bananas
2 small apples
3 small pears
4 kiwifruit
2 medium oranges
4 passionfruit
250g grapes
3 lemons
4 limes
6 small tomatoes
3 small red capsicums
2 fresh small
  red thai chillies
2 fresh long red chillies
1 bunch basil
2 bunches mint
1 bunch dill
1 bunch chives
2 bunches coriander
2 bunches flat-leaf parsley
30g baby rocket
60g baby spinach leaves
30g pea shoots
2 bunches green onions
  (need 16 onions)
1 cucumber

½ bunch celery
  (need 6 stalks)
200g baby beetroot
150g green beans
1 iceberg lettuce
2 cobs corn
115g baby corn
80g bean sprouts
350g watercress
170g asparagus
175g tenderstem broccoli
3 small carrots
4 flat mushrooms (320g)
3 small red onions
400g potatoes
400g sweet potato
150g butternut pumpkin
Ginger (about 35g knob)
1 bulb garlic
  (need 8 cloves)

MEAT & SEAFOOD
600g chicken breast fillet
200g lamb backstrap
200g beef rump steak
2 beef fillet steaks (250g)
220g lean beef mince
250g pork fillet
30g sliced prosciutto
80g shaved turkey
300g firm white fish fillets
250g small cooked prawns
150g shaved ham

MISCELLANEOUS
1 small loaf rye bread
1 packet wholemeal
  wraps
1 packet large wholemeal
  pitta bread

SHOPPING LIST WEEK 3

FRIDGE
1 x 200g tub skim-milk
  passionfruit-flavoured
  yogurt
4 x 100g tubs skim-milk
  fruit-flavoured yogurt
4 x 140g tubs skim-milk
  natural yogurt
1 x 200g carton ricotta
  cheese
1 x 250g tub low-fat
  cottage cheese
600ml carton skim milk
8 eggs
Small carton unsweetened
  apple juice

FRUIT & VEG
310g strawberries
2 medium bananas (400g)
5 small apples
4 small pears
400g rockmelon
250g grapes
4 kiwifruit
1 medium pink
  grapefruit (425g)
5 medium oranges
6 lemons
4 limes
250g grape tomatoes
125g cherry tomatoes
11 small tomatoes
3 small red capsicums
1 small green capsicum
2 cucumbers
1 medium eggplant (300g)
1 fresh small
  red thai chilli
1 fresh long red chilli
1 bunch fresh thyme
1 bunch oregano
1 bunch basil
1 bunch dill
4 bunches flat-leaf parsley
1 bunch coriander
1 bunch green onions

1 bunch chives
150g baby spinach leaves
40g baby rocket
2 baby cos lettuce
170g asparagus
1 small zucchini
½ bunch celery
  (need 4 stalks)
300g chinese cabbage
180g bean sprouts
100g snow peas
4 small brown onions
2 small red onions
150g mushrooms
150g butternut pumpkin
2 small carrots
3 medium potatoes (400g)
Ginger (need 30g knob)
1 bulb garlic
  (need 9 cloves)

MEAT & SEAFOOD
880g chicken breast fillet
300g beef rump steak
170g lean beef mince
6 back bacon rashers
30g sliced prosciutto
360g firm white fish fillets
650g uncooked king
  prawns

MISCELLANEOUS
1 x 800g loaf rye bread
30g black olives

Glossary

ALL-BRAN A cereal made from wheat bran.

BABY BEETROOT Whole beetroot, available in vacuum packs and jars.

BALSAMIC VINEGAR Deep rich brown vinegar made from Trebbiano grapes; has a sweet/sour flavour.

BABY BUK CHOY Sometimes called shanghai buk choy or white cabbage (pak kat farang); has a mildly acrid, distinctively appealing taste.

BASIL An aromatic herb; there are many types, but the most commonly used is sweet, or common, basil.

BEANS
four bean mix Made up of kidney beans, butter beans, chickpeas and great northern beans.
sprouts Also known as bean shoots; tender new growths of assorted beans and seeds germinated for consumption as sprouts. The most readily available are mung bean, soybean, alfalfa and snow pea sprouts. Sprout mixtures or tendrils are also available.
white A generic term we use for canned or dried cannellini, haricot, navy or great northern beans.

BREAD
english muffin A round teacake made from yeast, flour, milk, semolina and salt; often confused with crumpets. Pre-baked and sold packaged in supermarkets, muffins should be split open and toasted before eating.
pitta Also known as lebanese bread; wheat-flour pocket bread sold in large, flat pieces that separate into two thin rounds. Also available in small thick pieces called pocket pitta.
rye Made with or partly with rye flour. It can be light or dark in colour.
tortilla Thin, round unleavened bread originating in Mexico. Two kinds are available, one made from wheat flour and the other from corn.
wholemeal wraps Flat, thin, soft-textured, yeast-free bread made from wholemeal flour; available from supermarkets.

BUTTERMILK Originally the term given to the slightly sour liquid left after butter was churned from cream, today it is commercially made similarly to yogurt. Sold alongside all fresh milk products in supermarkets; despite the implication of its name, it is low in fat.

CAPERS The grey-green buds of a warm climate (usually Mediterranean) shrub, sold either dried and salted or pickled in a vinegar brine. Baby capers are also available. Capers should be rinsed well before using.

CAPSICUM Also known as bell pepper or, simply, pepper; can be green, yellow, red, orange or purplish-black. Discard seeds and membranes before use.

CHEESE
cottage Fresh, white, unripened curd cheese with a lumpy consistency and a mild, sweet flavour.
fetta A crumbly goat- or sheep-milk cheese having a sharp, salty taste.
ricotta Sweet, moist, white cow-milk cheese with a slightly grainy texture.

CHICKPEAS Also called garbanzos, hummus or channa; an irregularly round, sandy-coloured legume.

CORIANDER Also known as cilantro, pak chee or chinese parsley; a bright-green-leafed herb with a pungent flavour. Both stems and roots are also used in Thai cooking; wash well before chopping. Also available as seeds or ground; these must never be used to replace fresh coriander or vice versa, as the tastes are completely different.

CORNICHONS French for gherkin, a very small variety of cucumber.

COUSCOUS A fine, grain-like cereal product made from semolina; it is rehydrated by steaming or with the addition of a warm liquid and swells to three or four times its original size.

CORN THINS A thin crispbread made from corn; 97% fat free.

DRIED SWEETENED CRANBERRIES Also known as craisins. Can usually be substituted for or with other dried fruit in most recipes.

FISH FILLETS, FIRM WHITE Any firm boneless fish fillet, such as blue-eye, ling and snapper, are suitable to use.

GREEN ONION Also known as spring onion or scallion; an immature onion picked before the bulb has formed, having a long, bright green edible stalk.

LENTILS Dried pulses often identified by and named after their colour (red, brown, yellow); also known as dhal.

LINGUINE Known as flat spaghetti or little tongues because of its long, narrow shape.

MINCE Also known as ground meat.

MUSHROOMS If a recipe calls for an unspecified type of mushroom, use button, a small, cultivated white mushroom with a mild flavour.
flat Large and flat with a rich earthy flavour. Are sometimes misnamed field mushrooms, which are wild mushrooms.

MUSTARD
dijon Also known as french. Pale brown, creamy, distinctively flavoured, fairly mild French mustard.
wholegrain Also known as seeded. A French-style coarse-grain mustard made from crushed mustard seeds and dijon-style french mustard.

OIL
cooking-oil spray Use a cholesterol-free cooking spray made from canola oil.
vegetable Sourced from plants.

OREGANO, FRESH Also known as wild marjoram; has a woody stalk with clumps of tiny, dark green leaves that have a pungent, peppery aroma. Related to the mint family.

PARSLEY, FLAT-LEAF Also known as continental or italian parsley.

PAPPADUMS Dried cracker-like wafers made from a combination of lentil and rice flours, oil and spices.

PRAWNS Also known as shrimp.

PROSCIUTTO A kind of unsmoked Italian ham; salted, air-cured and aged, it is usually eaten uncooked.

ROCKET Also known as arugula, rugula and rucola; a peppery-tasting green leaf that can be used similarly to baby spinach leaves. Baby rocket leaves are both smaller and less peppery.

ROLLED OATS Flattened oat grain rolled into flakes and traditionally used for porridge. Instant oats are also available, but use traditional oats for baking.

SAUCES
cranberry Made of cranberries cooked in sugar syrup.
fish Also called naam pla or nuoc naam. Made from pulverised salted fermented fish (most often anchovies); has a pungent smell and strong taste, so use according to your taste.
hoisin A thick, sweet and spicy Chinese sauce made from salted fermented soybeans, onions and garlic. From Asian food shops and supermarkets.
oyster A thick, richly flavoured brown sauce made from oysters and their brine, and cooked with salt and soy sauce, and thickened with starches.
soy, japanese An all-purpose low-salt soy sauce made with more wheat than its Chinese counterparts; fermented in barrels and aged.
soy, light Fairly thin, pale and salty tasting; used in dishes in which the natural colour of the ingredients is to be maintained.
sweet chilli Mild tasting sauce made from red chillies, sugar, garlic and white wine vinegar.
teriyaki A Japanese sauce made from mirin, sugar, soy sauce, ginger and other spices.

SPICES
cajun A blend of herbs and spices including basil, paprika, tarragon, onion, fennel, thyme and cayenne.
cinnamon Dried inner bark of the shoots of the cinnamon tree; available in stick (quill) or ground form.

cloves Dried flower buds of a tropical tree; can be used whole or in ground form. Has a distinctively pungent and "spicy" scent and flavour.
cumin Also known as zeera or comino; has a spicy, nutty flavour. Available in seed form or dried and ground.
curry powder A blend of ground spices including dried chilli, cinnamon, mace, coriander, cumin, fennel, fenugreek, cardamom and turmeric. Choose mild or hot to suit your taste and the recipe.
fennel, ground Dried seeds having a licorice flavour, ground to a fine powder.
green peppercorns The soft, under-ripe berry that's usually preserved in brine. Has a fresh flavour that's less pungent than the berry in its other forms.
mixed spice A blend of ground spices usually consisting of cinnamon, allspice and nutmeg.
nutmeg The dried nut of an evergreen tree; it is available ground, or you can grate your own with a fine grater.
sumac A purple-red, astringent spice ground from berries growing on wild shrubs found in the Mediterranean; adds a tart, lemony flavour.
taco seasoning mix A packaged seasoning meant to duplicate the Mexican sauce made from oregano, cumin, chillies and other spices.
tandoori spice mix A blend of spices that imparts the well-known tandoori flavour from India. Includes paprika, cumin, coriander, turmeric, ginger, cinnamon, fenugreek, pepper, chilli, cardamom, caraway and spearmint.
turmeric Known for the golden colour it imparts to the dishes of which it's a part. Dried turmeric has a rich, woody aroma and a slightly bitter, musky taste.

SPINACH Also known as english spinach and, incorrectly, silver beet.

STOCK Available in cans, bottles or tetra packs and as cubes, powder or concentrated liquid. As a guide, 1 teaspoon of stock powder or 1 small crumbled stock cube mixed with 1 cup (250ml) water will give a fairly strong stock. Be aware of the salt and fat content of these stocks.

SUGAR
brown Soft, finely granulated sugar retaining molasses for its characteristic colour and flavour.
demerara Golden-coloured, small-grained crystal sugar.

TENDERSTEM BROCCOLI A cross between broccoli and chinese kale; long asparagus-like stems with a long loose floret, both completely edible. Resembles broccoli in look, but milder and sweeter in taste.

THYME, FRESH A basic herb of French cuisine; a member of the mint family, it has tiny grey-green leaves that give off a pungent minty, light-lemon aroma.

TOMATOES
cherry A very small, round tomato.
egg Also called plum or roma; are smallish, oval-shaped tomatoes.
paste Triple-concentrated tomato puree.
yellow teardrop A very small, yellow pear-shaped tomato.

UDON NOODLES Available fresh and dried, these broad, white Japanese wheat noodles are similar to the ones in homemade chicken noodle soup.

UNCOOKED SEAFOOD MIX A mix of uncooked, chopped seafood; available from fish markets and fishmongers.

WATERCRESS Also known as winter rocket; a slightly peppery, dark-green leaf vegetable. Highly perishable, so use as soon as possible after purchase.

WOMBOK Also known as chinese cabbage, peking or napa cabbage; elongated in shape with pale green, crinkly leaves.

YOGURT
skim-milk fruit-flavoured yogurt We used fruit-flavoured yogurt made with skim milk and sweetened artificially.
skim-milk natural yogurt We used natural yogurt with a fat content of less than 0.2 per cent.

ZUCCHINI also known as courgette; small green, yellow or white vegetable belonging to the squash family.

Conversion chart

MEASURES

One Australian metric measuring cup holds approximately 250ml; one Australian metric tablespoon holds 20ml; one Australian metric teaspoon holds 5ml.

The difference between one country's measuring cups and another's is within a two- or three-teaspoon variance, and will not affect your cooking results. North America, New Zealand and the United Kingdom use a 15ml tablespoon.

All cup and spoon measurements are level. The most accurate way of measuring dry ingredients is to weigh them. When measuring liquids, use a clear glass or plastic jug with the metric markings.

We use large eggs with an average weight of 60g.

DRY MEASURES

METRIC	IMPERIAL
15g	½oz
30g	1oz
60g	2oz
90g	3oz
125g	4oz (¼lb)
155g	5oz
185g	6oz
220g	7oz
250g	8oz (½lb)
280g	9oz
315g	10oz
345g	11oz
375g	12oz (¾lb)
410g	13oz
440g	14oz
470g	15oz
500g	16oz (1lb)
750g	24oz (1½lb)
1kg	32oz (2lb)

LIQUID MEASURES

METRIC	IMPERIAL
30ml	1 fluid oz
60ml	2 fluid oz
100ml	3 fluid oz
125ml	4 fluid oz
150ml	5 fluid oz (¼ pint/1 gill)
190ml	6 fluid oz
250ml	8 fluid oz
300ml	10 fluid oz (½ pint)
500ml	16 fluid oz
600ml	20 fluid oz (1 pint)
1000ml (1 litre)	1¾ pints

LENGTH MEASURES

METRIC	IMPERIAL
3mm	⅛ in
6mm	¼in
1cm	½in
2cm	¾in
2.5cm	1in
5cm	2in
6cm	2½in
8cm	3in
10cm	4in
13cm	5in
15cm	6in
18cm	7in
20cm	8in
23cm	9in
25cm	10in
28cm	11in
30cm	12in (1ft)

OVEN TEMPERATURES

These oven temperatures are only a guide for conventional ovens. For fan-forced ovens, check the manufacturer's manual.

	°C (CELSIUS)	°F (FAHRENHEIT)	GAS MARK
Very slow	120	250	½
Slow	150	275-300	1-2
Moderately slow	160	325	3
Moderate	180	350-375	4-5
Moderately hot	200	400	6
Hot	220	425-450	7-8
Very hot	240	475	9

Index

Published in 2008 by Bauer Media Books, Sydney
Bauer Media Books are published by Bauer Media Limited
54 Park St, Sydney
GPO Box 4088, Sydney, NSW 2001.
phone (02) 9282 8618; fax (02) 9126 3702
www.awwcookbooks.com.au

MEDIA GROUP

BAUER MEDIA BOOKS
Publishing Director – Gerry Reynolds
Publisher – Sally Wright
Editorial & Food Director – Pamela Clark
Creative Director – Hieu Chi Nguyen
Food Concept Director – Sophia Young
Director of Sales, Marketing & Rights – Brian Cearnes

Published and Distributed in the United Kingdom by Octopus Publishing Group
Endeavour House
189 Shaftesbury Avenue
London WC2H 8JY
United Kingdom
phone (+44)(0)207 632 5400; fax (+44)(0)207 632 5405
info@octopus-publishing.co.uk;
www.octopusbooks.co.uk

To order books:
telephone LBS on 01903 828 503
order online at
www.australian-womens-weekly.com
or www.octopusbooks.co.uk

Printed in Thailand
International foreign language rights, Brian Cearnes, Bauer Media Books
bcearnes@bauer-media.com.au

A catalogue record for this book is available from the British Library.
ISBN 978-1-90742-830-2
© Bauer Media Limited 2008
ABN 18 053 273 546
First published in 2008. Reprinted 2011, 2013.